To the people who inspired my work and this book: my patients. I am thankful to every person with whom I've been privileged to work. You have given me selfless learning, friendship, and inspiration throughout my career.

ABOUT THE AUTHOR

Anthony Yanni – clinician, health system chief medical officer, and pharmaceutical executive – is a transformative leader known for advocating and leading patient-centricity integration into global healthcare practices. He has been pivotal in integrating patient perspectives and real-world needs into pharmaceutical innovation and development, demonstrating the patient and business benefits.

Dr. Yanni holds an MD degree from Drexel University School of Medicine (formerly Hahnemann University), an MBA from the University of Massachusetts and a BS from the University of Scranton.

Table of Contents

FOREWORD .... **i**

INTRODUCTION **1**

CHAPTER 1 .... **11**

Please, Can You Hear Me?

CHAPTER 2 .... **20**

A New Idea, Some Friends, and a Lot of Luck

CHAPTER 3 .... **33**

Blindfolded and Swinging for The Fences

CHAPTER 4 .... **45**

This Bandana Is All I Have

CHAPTER 5 .... **57**

A Bluebird in The Sun

CHAPTER 6 .... **68**

The Patient as A Disruptor

CHAPTER 7 .... **82**

The Art of Culture

CHAPTER 8 .... **93**

Improving The Healthcare Ecosystem

CHAPTER 9 .... **103**

Building Consensus While Destroying Barriers

CHAPTER 10 .... **115**

A Call to Action

CONCLUSION **122**

APPENDIX A

OPERATIONAL TRANSFORMATION **134**

APPENDIX B

CULTURAL TRANSFORMATION **141**

The Power of Education

ACKNOWLEDGMENTS **149**

FOREWORD

My Path To The Patient

"It's tough to make predictions, especially about the future."
- Yogi Berra

I was a freshman in high school when my sister and her husband had their first child. I was the youngest of four children with three older sisters and growing up I often felt that I had four mothers. They took good care of me for the most part, with a regular sprinkling of keeping me in my place. In this instance, it was my youngest sister giving birth and while this was not my first experience with a sister having a child, it was nonetheless exciting. I was adult-ish as a high schooler, so Tommy was the first baby I could enjoy from a more mature perspective. And let's be honest, large, and close-knit Italian families look for reasons to celebrate and none is more natural than having a new member join the growing clan.

My sister lived close by, so every day was an opportunity to spend time with Tommy, watching him grow and develop. He was plump with a very light complexion and thin hair. He had a pleasant demeanor as an infant, with a smile as his default facial expression. However, within a few months I sensed concern in my sister and my parents. Tommy didn't seem to be progressing as he should. He was having difficulty sitting up and wasn't turning over on his own. When he did sit, he almost bent in half at his torso, and when we picked him up, his shoulders would rise – there was no muscle tone.

He had been to the pediatrician for regular check-ups, and the doctor reassured us that all looked okay. But by six months of age, it was clear Tommy was not well. He was no longer able to sit up without falling over – more like flopping over. With additional doctor visits and referrals to specialty centers, he underwent a muscle biopsy. Tommy had Spinal Muscular Atrophy or SMA.

I remember vividly the day they came home from the Children's Hospital having been given the news. It was as if a major life reset occurred. Every concern, every priority, every goal became organically reordered. Uncles and aunts, cousins, and neighbors all came to my parents' house. I remember everyone crying and feeling hopeless. What is SMA? How could he have it? He would have a significantly shorter life expectancy – how could that be? Looking back, it felt surreal. There we were crying, scared beyond what could be imagined, yet we really had no idea what was in store for us. Who could we turn to? Who would help? Who would listen? In retrospect, this experience was a significant Patient Centricity lesson I tucked away for future use.

∞ ∞ ∞

Tommy's experience was my first glimpse of a child with a rare disease and a very frightened family's reaction. My reaction. This was 1980. The World Wide Web and the internet were barely a gleam in anyone's eye. There was no ready way to research and to learn. You were completely, fully beholden to every single word being spoken by those who did know – the doctors and healthcare providers. I remember sitting in the exam room during visits, waiting for the doctors to arrive. The "jury" returning with a verdict. As they entered, we would watch their facial expressions trying to discern in a microsecond what was to come. Did they look pleased or downtrodden? High energy or low? We hung on every word.

There were so many appointments – doctors, testing, specialty centers. Time was no longer monitored by the tick-tock of a clock but instead by the cadence of appointments and the time between them. It was during those early years that I had the opportunity to attend some of the medical visits with Tommy. I saw up close the impact health care professionals can have on a patient and their family. I recall the feeling of hope, linked to the fear of what we might hear, as we arrived at the hospital for testing and appointments.

This mixture always resulted in a cocktail of high anxiety. I was in awe of the grace and wisdom of those caring for him. Their sensitive approach was balanced against a keen desire to be truthful in the delivery of their information. When the appointments were completed, even in the face of news we did not want to hear, we always left appreciative and with hope.

I knew I wanted to be one of those people. Those visits and experiences sparked an evolution within me. I was impressed with how these professionals carried themselves. How they were able to deliver sometimes terrible news, but with delicate compassion. Their eye contact, the tone of their voice, even their touch, at times, was remarkable.

I continue to be amazed at the amount of receptive messaging that happens in the world around us. I never forgot this as my career progressed and always tried to impart to residents, fellows and other students in the health professions, the importance of being aware of not only *what* you say to a patient and family but also *how* you deliver the message. Too often those in the healthcare system feel the need to always share how smart they are when interacting with patients. This can be seen as a cold, indifferent approach to care at times. Tempering the needs of our egos with an awareness of what the patient needs in that moment is a better recipe. They are watching everything; non-verbal messaging is coming through loud and clear. This was another lesson for me.

How do we create better processes, within pharma and within delivery systems, which encourage this? Humility, competence, and compassion integrated into our systems and our cultures. Never allowing for excuses to sacrifice one in favor of the others.

Up to that point, in my mid-to-late teens, I had a strong interest in science but was considering a career in law. My family would say (and still do) I will debate anything, pointing out with an eye roll that I'm not a fan of losing. But after those experiences there was no way I could do anything other than medicine.

These experiential learnings, from the time I was 16 years old, afforded me the opportunity later to see the pharmaceutical industry and the healthcare delivery system from different perspectives. As I evolved through my career and was exposed to each of the systems – clinical practice, chief medical officer, pharmaceutical companies – I viewed patients and their families as partners, not simply consumers. The traditional approach – we will build your solutions and the systems for you – simply didn't make sense to me. All too often, each of those systems says "okay, you do your thing, I'll do my thing and when we're done, we'll just stitch it together and the patients will love it." But that just doesn't work; it's a siloed approach that cannot deliver the best for patients.

Our Roots Inform Our Lives

I am the grandson of Italian immigrants with both sets of grandparents immigrating to the United States in the early 1900's. In fact, they didn't all come to America at the same time. Instead, the men came over first, settled in Scranton, Pennsylvania, landed jobs in the coal mines, and sent money back to Calabria, Italy for the family to sustain themselves. When they made it to the States, they saved money by staying with relatives who had arrived a few years earlier. When they accumulated enough, they would send for their families to join them.

For my maternal grandfather, everything changed eight months after arriving. My grandmother was pregnant when he left for America and several months later, he received a letter from her announcing the birth of their son. A huge celebration took place in the neighborhood in Scranton, with relatives and friends toasting his new child. Two weeks later he received another letter from my grandmother informing him the child had died – on the very day they were celebrating in Scranton.

It was that day he decided to send for the entire family, explaining to those around him: "We are going to laugh together or cry together, but we will be together." This story has been passed down from my grandmother to my parents and to my sisters and I, and it speaks to the importance of family, indeed any support network, as well as the great suffering endured in those early years due to the difficult decisions that had to be made.

What was unique about this story was that despite a singular reason for their sadness – the death of a child – their suffering was quite different. My grandmother, across the ocean, had to face the reality of a child she had held and fed having died. My grandfather, never seeing the child, surely was faced with guilt and the desire to be there to support my grandmother. Perspective and context are quite meaningful and thousands of miles in distance is only one small example of why we need to be acutely aware of the diversity we face with each patient and their family story.

My family remained in Scranton, and I lived in a mostly Italian neighborhood. Scranton is a city I've described as a place where the people give far more than should be expected and expect far less than they deserve. It was a great place to grow up.

My parents were watchful but not hovering. Both were children of the Depression, and their very poor upbringing shaped them as adults. My father would repeatedly say to all the family that he was so poor growing up that "the only thing we didn't eat on the chicken was the cluck." We would laugh but recognize the truth in that statement.

We didn't have a lot of money growing up, but I never felt poor. There were periods where money was more of a concern than others, but my father was a contractor and always managed to provide. More than food and water, he provided me and my sisters with a perspective on life that still sticks with me today. He taught us early and often to never link money with happiness. "You'll always be disappointed," he would say. He taught me that to build an empire of money and material things is not as sturdy as one built of family, friends, character, and Faith.

One day shortly after graduating from medical school, my father and I were getting a coffee at a Starbucks and while we were waiting, he said to me: "Always remember you are one of the very fortunate. Never forget those that have a more difficult life. If you see someone who can't afford your services – remember where you came from and care for them anyway." This 15-second statement reinforced two decades of upbringing in a simple, direct way. To this day I have no idea why it came up at that moment, but it had a reinforcing impact on my professional approach and in some ways, became a central thread that runs through my concept of Patient Centricity.

When I was accepted to medical school and told my grandmother, you would think I was some sort of 80s rock star. She couldn't believe a grandson of hers would be a doctor. In her eyes it was me, and then Sinatra. Springsteen and Bon Jovi didn't even make the list. And for those who know Italians well – or are Italian – you know our affinity for doctors is like moths to a flame.

To describe my medical school days as financially strained would be an understatement. My parents lacked resources for large checks to be written, so I relied on high interest student loans not only to pay for tuition but also to support my living expenses. I had no extra cash . . . but what did I really need? No big deal, right?

My second year of medical school I shared an apartment with a friend from college who was attending podiatry school. We had a nice high-ceilinged apartment with huge windows in Center City Philadelphia. The place looked beautiful but, in the winters, it was unaffordable to heat. Our only solution: bundle up. I would study with two to three layers of clothing on – two pairs of pants, two shirts, a sweatshirt, and a coat, two pairs of socks, a winter hat, and always with gloves on. When my roommate and I needed to talk, we would go into the closet and sit next to the water heater to warm up a bit. At times, it was literally freezing. When I tell my kids that story, they think it is more legend than fact. But it's 100% true.

I got engaged during my second year of medical school, a big move for a very poor guy. I "popped the question" in the living room of my apartment. We survived paycheck to paycheck, eating often enough at my middle sister's house that she began calling us as she planned meals for the week, adjusting the menu based on our feedback. We had no shame, even joining her and her family on (free) vacations. A big night out for us was a free meal at my sister's and a rented movie. Such great days.

I left medical school in 1992 with a whopping $107,000 of debt and a residency salary of around $28,000, as I recall. My wife found a job, we rented an apartment, and lived well – basically having everything we needed and wanting nothing we didn't have.

I always found the professional journey – anyone's – fascinating. What is seen as absolute to a younger person – the current condition – is a product of years of toil, stress, and uncertainty. I often interact with students and Fellows who seek career guidance and input. Usually, I point to three things.

First, always remain curious. We tend to focus on what we know – our strengths. However, in healthcare, what we don't know can be more important to recognize. There's a vast world out there; recognize that most everyone has something to contribute. Ask questions, listen, and you will learn.

Second, set a path, but stay open to new ideas and course corrections along the way. In any 10-year period, reflect on how the world has changed. To lock out these evolutions from consideration because of a predetermined path is a mistake. Keep your eyes open and continue to move forward, more aware, and with the freedom to adjust your journey.

Third, treat your career like chess and not checkers; always look a few moves ahead. If you are chasing the best title and the most money in the next six months, you likely will end up in a place you never intended to be – a place, perhaps, less desirable. You need to think about your career in a more strategic way.

As I reflect on my career, I think I most definitely followed these rules.

When I left medical school, I decided to specialize in internal medicine. My goal from the beginning was to spend time in the exam room and at the bedside with patients. I enjoyed getting to know the individuals and their families and these connections energized me. I spent more than a dozen years treating patients directly and during that time developed an interest in business. This led to managing a large multi-doctor private practice and eventually becoming Chief of Internal Medicine and then Chief Medical Officer of a hospital system. These unanticipated, but added, responsibilities gave me valuable experiences in healthcare from multiple perspectives involving multiple participants: patient, provider, healthcare systems, payers, government.

From there I joined Pharma, first working in vaccine development then to my current work.

One of the many "pleasures" I've found on my path to Patient Centricity was in the thousands of patients I've treated over the years; each with their own story and life lesson. Judges and teachers, truck drivers and politicians, business owners and stay-at-home moms and dads, professors, and grandmas.

Their stories provided me with an incredible and privileged learning opportunity. In many cases, they illustrated for me the spirit and determination you find in countless individuals. At one point, I even met a gentleman who had been awarded the Congressional Medal of Honor in World War Two. An amazing man with an amazing story.

The Path to Patient Centricity

In the years after Tommy's diagnosis so much changed. My sister and her husband transformed Tommy's bedroom into a hospital room. I saw up close my sister becoming an experienced "nurse," managing a tracheostomy, home ventilation, IV infusions when necessary. Through all of this and as of this writing not a single complaint from either of them was heard. The privilege and burden of being a caregiver was seared into my understanding.

Unfortunately, during my journey my nephew Tommy's journey sadly ended. A life of joy and struggle, he passed away in 2007 at the age of 27. In 1982, his brother, Tim, was born; also afflicted with SMA. They grew up together, closer than any two siblings I've ever seen. When Tommy passed, it was a difficult transition for us all but especially for Tim. Tim is now 42 and shares the same joys and struggles as his brother. However, today, there are treatments available for SMA. While the impact on Tim's advanced disease is measured, he has benefited from improved care and early intervention when he's not feeling well. However, those born today with SMA will have a much different life ahead of them.

This is an example of vocal patient advocacy and pharma teams integrating their voice into their programs. It is an example of incredible science delivered by incredible people transforming hope into reality. All of this further energizes me in my work and my evangelization of Patient Centricity. We can learn. We can evolve. We can be even better tomorrow than we are today.

My path before and since the days of medical school has been a treasure hunt – not always knowing for sure the choices made would be correct but always trying to make the most of what was discovered. I could never have predicted the journey; no GPS was available to enter into it where and when I thought I should arrive.

Looking back, given a thousand guesses after completing residency in 1995, I would have never imagined my current work in Patient Centricity. The treasure hunt has been an amazing adventure with each "find" along the path bringing immeasurable joy, a lot of learning, a fair share of sorrows, but no regrets.

INTRODUCTION

When I wrote this book, I had in mind primarily those who work in and around new medicine development, those in the healthcare delivery system, and of course, patients and caregivers. It is not written as a conclusion of a journey but the path to a destination. It's my hope that the perspective I share will begin a conversation, motivate leaders to embark on change and perhaps, in some way, gain the acknowledgement that there is room for improvement.

I realize this topic of new medicine development and the delivery of care is quite complex and Patient Centricity, in isolation, will not provide a comprehensive solution to the many challenges facing our healthcare system. Neither Patient Centricity nor this book is intended to offer a road to healthcare Nirvana. Instead, it is about progress toward that goal and respect for the very people who rely on our efforts. We should not expect to solve this problem in one quick step nor should we be frozen in time, ignoring necessary change because the pessimists diminish the importance of it. Patient Centricity can improve many aspects of medicine development and care delivery. It's not the answer to everything but it's a leap worth taking towards better outcomes.

As you proceed through this book, you will meet the people and read the stories that inspired both my learnings and my motivation toward my work in Patient Centricity. Through these examples I will discuss the importance of improved communication among family members and caregivers as well as within the healthcare delivery system. The concept of working your network, any network, to facilitate the snatching of every opportunity, no matter how small and to move toward the goal of Patient Focused Medicine Development and Delivery (PFMDD) – the integration of the patient perspective into *all* processes in the developmental continuum.

I will emphasize and re-emphasize the critical role culture plays in organizational movement toward a consistent process that will support PFMDD in a sustainable way. In the appendices I will share some details around many of the programs that I believe will help you get there.

I will also discuss the need to approach Patient Centricity from an enterprise perspective and to do so with senior leadership involved. In essence, what will be discussed is a change management approach, identifying barriers patients have in getting care (e.g.: access to treatments and treaters), how to convert those with whom we work utilizing a "Head, Heart and Hands" approach, and the importance of developing meaningful and balanced metrics to convince the business of the value that this work contributes.

Finally, I hope to make clear the connection I see between

Pharma and the delivery system; both so critical to patients receiving the care they deserve. While this connection may seem abstract, I hope to convince the reader that connectivity is important to acknowledge if we are to address the complexity of delivering care to people in need. The common point between the two systems is Patient Centricity.

This book was inspired by the many patients who selflessly showed me the way, leading me down a path in my career to this very point. I truly hope that patients who may read this can connect with the passion I feel for this work, the lessons that motivated me and together, find a more powerful voice to join in this necessary evolution.

Throughout the book I refer to "patients" as individuals or as groups of individuals. However, I would be remiss if I didn't highlight the importance of, and my respect for, the many Patient Advocacy Groups that exist in support of patients. They do so in a general way across disease areas as well as within specific disease areas. These organizations are led by dedicated individuals, many of whom are patients or caregivers themselves. Much of my work and the work of my teams has been in collaboration with these groups and any resulting success is shared with them. They have been, and continue to be, great partners who represent their patients honorably and with determination to help find meaningful solutions.

There have been many books written about the challenges in drug development and healthcare delivery and perhaps even more about the heroic efforts of the people working in both of those industries. However, to my knowledge, none have been written about Patient Centricity being the common thread to creating momentum for change that patients deserve and can actively take part in.

I hope my respect for Pharma and the healthcare delivery system comes through clearly. Most importantly my respect for the workers. However, it is necessary to discuss the shortcomings to ignite change with an eye toward a solution. The stories I share are part of my path to my current work – my inspiration. They provided me with perspective that spans medicine development, healthcare delivery, change management, and the importance of culture. I do realize this is a broad focus for a single brief book. However, these experiences gave me the ability, I believe, to discuss the applicability of patient centricity and the importance of culture as a foundation across these areas.

One of the principles of this work is a shared path forward. I see none of it as competitive and have tried to openly share my work, processes, and metrics whenever possible. While a deeper dive into some areas is possible, I do believe the shared ideas and methods could be helpful for those interested in beginning similar processes. I also look forward to better ideas and processes from others and have no issue implementing them if they improve the impact on patients.

Throughout this book, whenever possible, I have intentionally left vague the "where" and "who"; that is, I have no desire to implicate or blame anyone or any institution for challenges that exist broadly across the industries in which I have worked. I am far less vague with my gratitude for those who provided me with the runway to create this work and the support needed to continue it.

While all patient stories are true, other than when given specific authorization, the patient identities have been altered and, in most cases, year, location, and the like have been omitted to support an additional level of anonymity.

Over the years, to gain more background information for my work, I spoke to leaders of other industries, including defense contractors, automobile manufacturers, restaurant owners, and retailers. The general response was a surprise that our customers were not meaningfully involved in the processes we utilized in medicine development. Each had specific methods in place to better understand the customer and, importantly, to ensure that the input was considered throughout the production and delivery cycle.

When I spoke to patients over the years, many were satisfied and haven't given much thought to the challenges I raise. However, those who rely most on the systems because of chronic or serious illnesses had significant concerns and those concerns were the basis for the Patient Centricity effort that I have focused on for nearly two decades.

One final point on those conversations that have motivated me. Some of the most convincing have been with healthcare providers, scientists, nurses, and commercial folks. They want improved systems to help them achieve their professional goals. They want to understand the patient's needs more fully, have time to learn more about patient barriers to care, and opportunities for meaningful human contact. There is momentum all around us – we must grasp it.

For those who may stumble upon this book and begin to read or for those unfamiliar with some of the challenges and proposed solutions, Patient Centricity may be a new term for you, however, what it stands for is not. Patient Centricity impacts all of us. If you are lucky enough to not have taken a medicine or interacted with the healthcare system to this point in your life or in the life of a loved one – congratulations and God Bless. But I'll say, that won't last. We are all current or future patients. Many will be caregivers. Patient Centricity is not about "them" it's about "us."

Once we acknowledge the reality of the situation, I hope it raises an eyebrow for every reader. We need to take part – all of us – if this transformation to a much more patient focused medicine development and delivery system is to move toward success. If we wait until each one of us is impacted before we say "enough" then we've lost a good bit of time and a lot of opportunity to make a positive impact. This call to action doesn't require you to get out of bed every Saturday morning and drive long distances. It requires you to recognize there is a problem, that it affects all of us at some point in our lives and that solutions are available.

However, the solutions do require your participation. We can force change through our refusal to accept the status quo in the interactions we have with the healthcare system. By asking the important questions of the systems that deliver services to ensure they understand that what we all expect is not only treatment but care. Importantly, real people – patients, caregivers, workers - were the motivation behind this work.

What I share as successful efforts can most definitely be improved upon. There were certainly many disappointments interspersed along the way. My intention is not to boast of a solution but to stimulate more ideas to move forward on this journey. Many times, I write of deficiencies in pharma and delivery systems, but I did try to provide balance with a perspective of someone who has been on both sides of the exam table, behind a desk as a hospital administrator, and in the trenches of new medicine development. I readily accept a share of any responsibility for systemic shortcomings. To arrive at a solution requires discernment of the problems, however I do not want to imply everything is broken in every system and every company. On the contrary, I discuss examples of excellent care that, unfortunately, were not captured and multiplied by the very systems in which they occurred.

To be sure, this change will not happen quickly – but it needs to begin. We have methods to ignite this evolution; methods that will not materially increase costs or negatively affect services. Quite the contrary, these changes will improve the services and likely decrease costs through a more motivated and retained work force, more focused medicine development aligned with the needs of patients, and harmony across delivery systems. You'll read about some of these efforts in more detail: an annual Patient Centricity Month and the Patient Centricity University are examples. Both are designed to be big and impactful, attracting team members from across the world, to inspire and be inspired, to learn and to teach.

Imagine the impact if payers, retailers, and government agencies were to adopt or improve systems that evaluated and delivered services that were aligned with the needs of those it was designed to serve! Will payers not benefit from a cultural change where their team members go to work each day, recognizing the important work they do for patients, eliminating the cage-match that seemingly exists between doctors and the prescriptions they write – patients, often passively, sitting on the sidelines hoping they receive what they believe they need? Do we think that is a comfortable dynamic for those in the insurance world?

For those organizations that look at this book with ridicule and the idea that you are already doing these things. Great … please share your successes so we can all benefit. For those who say it and do not have the evidence, I ask you, respectfully, to have a deeper look and begin to discern what can be improved. At Astellas, there exists a tagline for Patient Centricity, "Patients Are WHY™." They are the reason for the day. Simply ask yourselves as leaders, have I supported my teams in their reason for the day?

Amazing people, every day, sacrifice a great deal to develop and deliver treatments to people in need. This book, I hope, will stimulate leaders to seek out and celebrate the "great" and help those individuals persist in their commitment to their art.

The pages ahead are a reflection on the many patients and caregivers who have taught me so many lessons throughout my career and life. Selfless giving, often at the worst of times for them, is heroic and should be remembered. The best way to do so, in my opinion, is to make their stories actionable. Accept their learnings and with vigor begin to address the issues they faced. If we do that successfully, we will have constructed permanent monuments to their teachings and provided a much better system of care for those that follow.

Anthony Yanni

Naples, Florida

CHAPTER 1

Please, Can You Hear Me?

The Importance Of Communication Within Families And Caregiver Networks

I was nervous, a beehive of nerves. All the time. My short white coat weighed 15 pounds from the books in the pockets and medical equipment stuffed wherever it fit. I can't say I was tired because the feeling others would describe as fatigue was my baseline. Instead, I would notice that rare day when I slept enough to feel rested. This was the life of a 3rd year medical student in 1990. Days slipped into nights and time of day was irrelevant. There were entire days where all I saw was the glow of artificial lighting, and those days sometimes lasted 36 hours. It was a period of learning like none I have experienced before or since.

My job was to be the first and last team member to visit my patients in the hospital, spending a good deal of time with each patient every day. My primary focus was to know more about their condition than any other doctor or student on the team. That meant gathering lab data, writing a progress note, and reviewing the books I was loaded down with to be sure I was up to date on the treatment for anything that may come my way, whether it be pancreatitis or the post op care of a patient who had undergone vascular surgery.

Every day in the mid-morning we would gather as a team – 10 to 12 of us – to "make rounds" on our patients as a group. Fellows, Residents, 4th year students and 3rd year students would be asked questions by the attending physician – in ascending order – with the least experienced fielding the first round of queries. The topics would range from diagnosis, to changes in the patient's condition over the last 24 hours, to care plans – all in the presence of the patient and each other. On display was my brilliance or stupidity – every day. The thought of it still brings on a tinge of anxiety. You did all you could to learn everything about your patients. This obviously involved enormous amounts of technical learning, but I was slow to realize that I was also the most connected human on the team with the patient.

Anna taught me that lesson. She was a young woman in her early 30s. She had a rare lung tumor and was progressively getting worse. Her family involved themselves intensely and loved her dearly. They were with her most of the day and when I visited, I saw the family network and appreciated the love. All seemed well.

However, one late evening when I stopped in to see Anna before going home, she asked me to sit for a while. She became emotional and began to cry while she explained her frustration.

Anna's family members, while well-intentioned, were unknowingly creating a great deal of stress for her. They would constantly pressure her to eat; something she had difficulty doing because of the tumor compressing her esophagus. She would politely decline, but they would insist. There were at least two occasions when food lodged in her esophagus, which required an endoscopic procedure to have it removed.

"I've told them so many times that I just can't swallow. But they don't hear me," she said through sobs. They associated eating with her health improving and wanted to believe she was getting better. Anna asked if I would talk to them, which I did the next day. They were extremely kind and good people. They heard my concerns and they seemed to understand the seriousness of Anna's condition. But they believed they were helping her by being "positive." Encouraging her to eat sent her a message that they believed she could get better. Nothing would change their thinking in the ensuing days.

This patient and family dynamic – which I saw almost every day – was not as it appeared. I realized that while I knew in detail her electrolytes and urine outputs, I had known little about how she felt and what she wanted. She felt frustrated. She wanted someone to listen to her.

Although I didn't have a name for it at the time, Anna gave me my earliest lesson in Patient Centricity.

My second lesson, unfortunately, came just two weeks later. I was making my morning rounds long before sunrise when my pager went off and I was called urgently to Anna's room. As I approached, I could hear voices and the hurried nature of the conversation. The beeps of cardiac monitoring were loud and there was barely room for me to fit as I entered the room. I felt a little bit of panic as I saw her having difficulty breathing. They were preparing to put in a breathing tube, and she was clearly frightened – her eyes moving quickly around the room as she worked very hard for each breath.

Then Anna taught me a lesson I will never forget. As she looked toward the door and saw me, she extended her left arm for me to hold her hand. With a dozen people in the room providing the best care available, all she wanted was someone to hold her hand. I immediately held her hand tightly as she quickly calmed down. Forty-five seconds later they were ready to insert her breathing tube and I'll never forget the look she gave me. It was a bit of a nod, almost an "I'm good" look, then she closed her eyes, let go of my hand and she was intubated.

∞ ∞ ∞

That was 33 years ago, and I honestly cannot count the number of times in my career I think back to Anna and how she taught me that to truly understand a patient – each patient – you need to listen. You need to be present.

Can I say now that 45 seconds made all the difference? Probably not. It was the hours spent with Anna that led to those 45 seconds that did. But can I say my current work in Patient Centricity would be a reality today without recognizing the importance of those 45 seconds? No way.

The message to me was that every moment counts, and each interaction can link to something big and beautiful, if you're open to it. The key, I think, is to take the time to listen and reflect so we can apply the learnings to help those that follow. That is the essence of Patient Centricity.

Each journey, despite the commonality of the start, is unique. Even more complex is applying these learnings and concepts at an industry level. How can a pharmaceutical company possibly know what patients need and where they see value in their next treatment without including them in the process and listening to them?

Despite all my training, despite technology that allows us to peek into organs and the very genes from which each of us is built, I can't possibly understand the patient's experience – any patient experience – without taking the time to listen.

Think about it; nearly every other industry approaches their customers in a fully integrated way. You'd be hard pressed to identify a product that has not had input from thousands of customers prior to wide-scale production. Why has Pharma been so slow to understand this? Patient Centricity is the necessary humility of Pharma to acknowledge we don't know everything. We may (and do) have the smartest scientists, doctors, and businesspeople working within our walls to cure diseases, ease suffering, and prolong life. But something is missing; there's a glaring gap in our approach. The patient.

Patient Centricity is not some abstract concept or vague idea or PR phrase. It's as real as Anna. It's both the science and the art of medicine. It is the critical ingredient in the complex process of developing and delivering new solutions for patients.

The Multi-Dimensionality of Patient Centricity

However, we should not think of this as a one-dimensional approach. Despite its origins, Patient Centricity is not a function isolated to Pharma; it begins at home, with those closest to us. When I think about the disconnect Anna felt with her loving family it was not due to a lack of caring. A good deal of it was due to the lack of open communication.

Having spent a good deal of time in the exam room and at the bedside, I have often experienced this dynamic. Family members and patients are physically together but not emotionally aligned. When alone with the families I have frequently heard them struggle with the reality of what they are facing, not willing to discuss it with the patient for fear they will discourage and upset them. Yet, in private conversations, the patient often shares their frustration with their family member's lack of understanding – or acknowledgement – of the seriousness of their condition and the acceptance that the road ahead is uncertain. In every instance, this added enormous pressure on the patient *and* the family members.

I understand every situation is unique, but in my experience, honest exchanges – a patient centric approach – would best serve all those involved. This does not need to be forced; simple conversations and listening often allows families to mirror the level of interaction the patient is asking for. To be sure, patients most often have a keen awareness of their condition – even those that appear to be more passive in their care. They understand body language and testing implications. They understand the urgency of treatment and the attention from family and friends. Rarely have I seen a situation where the family and patient disconnect occurred and the patient was not more aware – and accurate – in the assessment of their condition.

This is not a criticism. On the contrary, I and my family have been in this situation many times, believing that positivity and avoidance of difficult conversations is the best path. While it may be the most traveled path, I know now it is not always the best path.

To be clear, open communication should not replace hope and empathy with brutal negativity. There is a balance in there that we reach only through listening to the patient and a comfort level with difficult conversations. Medical education, when I was in school, didn't dive too deeply into this nuance. Anna and I crossed paths very early in my training. At that time, seeing many patients with no support network at all, if a patient had one I assumed all was good. It took many years of observation and lessons from patients to focus my understanding on the reality and not the fiction I falsely believed to be true.

In our early clinical days in medical school the diversity of approaches to patient interactions among my peers was amazing. In retrospect, it was akin to a museum of behaviors. Some students learned to be truthful without thought; always revealing their goal to be the smartest in the room and not considering how their textbook approach landed on those most impacted from their words. Others deflected the uncomfortable feeling of these conversations leaving the patient to wonder what the future held. In training, we were overwhelmed with learning facts, but the art was something only learned by the most astute students observing the best practitioners in the clinic setting. Add an overwhelming schedule with little time to spend with each patient and both the forest and the trees are often missed.

Beyond a support network (if fortunate enough to have one), care of a patient requires a series of highly specialized businesses and teams dedicated to a singular goal: delivering high value care and solutions to patients, developed with patients, and delivered in a way that respects them as individuals. The systems today are not adequately aligned and have not fully developed processes to address this singular goal.

Pharma is front and center in this and patient centricity is the method, in my view, to effect positive change. Where does the delivery system sit in this dilemma? I delve into this further in chapter 9 but briefly, the system has fallen quite short in prioritizing patient needs. They have unfortunately transformed into businesses that treat patients, but often at the expense of caring for people and their families. This is not an intentional deficiency; these are amazingly compassionate people delivering care. We need only look at the selfless commitment during the 2019 pandemic. However, these are issues of a system in transition from where it was to where it will be and unfortunately the current state is unsteady in my view.

A lot of what I've written here is a bit heavy, but that is only a piece of the story. Patient centricity is about hope, it is a better path to our approach to providing care and healing. And yes, on some occasions, it is about helping individuals pass from this life to the next. There can be no distinction between the two as it is a continuum – and individual needs and expectations should be at the center of both.

Most of my work has been about applying these principles to new medicine development for patients. It's a process that can be applied across disease areas and across companies – including the delivery systems. However, it is important that we recognize the interactions on a personal level that occur as we support those in need. Through it all, we should acknowledge the need for patient-centered communication.

Each patient's journey is complex and very personal; there is no standard route. Patient centricity is about learning and listening. It's about both organizations and individuals. But it's mostly about the patient and their unique ability to help us develop solutions, as well as our ability to provide them with the care and support they need to heal and to be at peace as their journey progresses.

CHAPTER 2

A New Idea, Some Friends, and a Lot of Luck

Utilizing And Leveraging Your Network

Sometimes success happens because of good planning; other times it's simply luck. I always believed that most good things come to people from both; persistent hard work over long periods of time allowing for luck to gently land in your path and have a positive impact. That is my story as I worked to develop an approach to Patient Centricity in Pharma.

One Wednesday I arrived at our company headquarters in Paris. I flew in the day before and I was still a bit tired from the time change. I came to the office at 7AM, drank a couple of dark roast Nespresso cups of coffee to begin the day. The office was a short walk from a very nice boutique hotel in the 8th Arrondissement and the spring day was cloudy but warm.

Soon after settling in at a desk, I got a message from the Head of Research: "Be ready to be on the move today. We're trying to get you some time with the head of R&D." The head of R&D was a big boss, which I was not. In fact, I was quite junior at that time. I became a bit anxious about the uncertainty of the message but felt ready for what I believed would be a rare opportunity.

I knew there was no guarantee this would happen; the head of R&D's schedule that day and most days was fully booked. In fact, this Wednesday he had meetings at a facility 20 miles outside of Paris. The plan was to allow me some "face time" with him to explain the process I developed which integrates the patient perspective into our drug research programs.

I had started this work 18 months earlier having been initially in a role designed to assign "medical value" to early research programs. It became clear after a few months in that role that I was adding no value to decision-making. There was no set process and no patients involved. I approached my manager at the time and explained to her that the current work was nearly useless. To her credit (for which I am forever thankful) she took the time to ask me where I saw this heading. It was then that I wrote on a whiteboard the earliest version of what is now our approach to Patient Centricity. A few weeks later she introduced me to a few senior leaders and after pitching my idea they gave me one headcount and a very small budget and said: "Give it a go and we'll see what it looks like."

I took the show on the road and met with any research team that was willing to listen. Most wanted to throw me out of the room when I suggested changing the way they evaluate their projects. It really wasn't making a change but adding a component: patient insights. Finally, after many meetings and pitch sessions, one research team agreed, and we completed an analysis that included insights from patient discussions. They loved it, and within 18 months the process was beginning to become global within our company.

Through this work is how I "accidently" met the head of research of our company. It started with his chief of staff, who brought us together (again, for which I am forever thankful). I shared with her the process and my vision. She had never seen or heard of anything like it and thought it was worth pursuing. She was very focused on the patient in her thinking and her work and wanted me to meet with her boss. He had just started in this role and was literally touring the global facilities to meet with teams.

She was aware I had tried to schedule a call with him, and he declined the first meeting I offered, preferring to defer it to "sometime in the future." However, his chief of staff felt strongly about this work, so she scheduled him to a conference room when he was visiting the facility where I worked. I remember his facial expression when he walked in; he was perplexed as to what he was doing there with only me in the room. He paused, turned back toward the hallway as if he had entered the wrong room. He looked at his chief of staff. She nodded and said, "this is the correct room." She introduced me and off I went with the presentation. Thirty minutes later we were done, and I later learned that as he was leaving, he said to his chief of staff – "thanks for making that happen."

Nearly two years later, I was in Paris and this same head of research had arranged for me to meet his boss – the head of R&D – and pitch the idea with the goal of gaining his support.

A driver was to take me to the facility outside of Paris where he was in meetings, and I was to chat with him on our ride back to Paris. The same chief of staff who facilitated my meeting with the Head of Research called me and said: "Be in front of the building at 12:15. A driver will meet you there and take you to where he is. Go to the third floor and there will be two chairs by the elevator. Sit and wait for him to finish." I felt as though I was being handed a script from a movie.

I followed the instructions to the letter, waited about an hour and a half, and sure enough, out he came. I had been in his presence before, but had not really interacted with him directly, so I was unsure what to expect. Gracious as always, he saw me and said "Hey Anthony. I hear you're giving me a ride back to Paris." I think that was the only time in my many trips to Paris over the years that I prayed for traffic! We sat in the back seat and talked the entire ride. By the time we reached the Arc de Triomphe he said, "Do it."

That was more than 10 years ago and it began my efforts to build a formal and fully endorsed Patient Centric process that could positively impact the way our industry develops medicines. It "took a village," a lot of persistence, and some very kind people to make it happen. People I will never forget.

∞ ∞ ∞

Can Patient Centricity be applied to other pharma and biotech companies as well as other players in the healthcare ecosystem – payers, insurers, delivery systems? The answer is absolutely "yes." But be prepared for resistance.

Despite the seemingly unifying theme of patient centricity, people are often resistant to change. This is especially true for senior leaders. I realize this is an electrifying statement and many will disagree before considering my rationale. It's not about their character, it's about their context. What is their motivation to change something drastically? Many have already reached the senior-most levels in their careers – or close to it. Change, at that point, can be more risk than reward. Incremental change? Sure. Drastic change when things are crumbling. Yep. But major change proactively? Not too often. It requires a leader willing to look forward and not backward; willing to accept risk to address change that will transition from something good to something great. I was fortunate to be surrounded by such leaders.

However, there wasn't anyone throwing roses in my path. I had to fight for a seat at the table and I used an extensive network of "believers" to provide me access to the decision-makers when I didn't have access myself. Without them, this would not have been achievable. I believed in the value of this process and always pushed forward; if one door closed I either knocked until the annoyed door keeper responded or found another way in. The chief medical officer of the same pharma company once said to me "Anthony, you are the most persistent person I've ever met. You're relentless." I'm not sure he meant it as a compliment, but it was accurate.

Facing the Bell Curve of Change Management

In my world, I was facing a bell curve. About 2.5% were early adopters, who would be interested in just about any reasonable new idea. There were another 2.5% who would be against virtually any innovation you might suggest, just because it was new. Then there's 95% in the middle who had to be convinced, but once convinced, they simply wanted their life to be easier, their work more successful, and get to their kids' after-school activities. As a starting point I concentrated on finding who was in the first group – including leaders who were willing to listen – and get them to say, "I'm with you, go ahead and try."

I didn't obsess over the 2.5% that were likely to be opposed, but I did prepare to address them. Essentially, their opposition came from two sources. One is the fear that we're doing something that's going to put them out of business or make them less relevant. The second is, if we're successful, they might be questioned as to why they didn't think of it first. I may not have agreed with their opposition – I believed in our position – but I listened to it.

For the 95% who I believed would be amenable to a new approach, I had to think of ways to convince them; methods to overcome whatever skepticism they may have, get them to drop their shields of fear, and become part of the solution versus becoming apathetic toward the idea.

This is where belief, commitment, and persistence enter. People see this. They feel it. The "cool," often emotionally detached vibe, that leaders try to convey needs to be replaced, at least temporarily, with passion for all to see. If I didn't display my belief in this, it would have failed early because I needed to build an internal coalition relatively quickly all screaming in unison "we need patient input!" It was a hard slog. I would put my virtual armor on every day so the arrows being flung in my direction would bounce off me.

As my new teams interacted more regularly with internal customers, we adopted a positioning that accommodated questions. We listened actively and attentively to understand and acknowledge any concerns, sharing what we believed was unique and impactful in our approach and how it was not similar to what was already being done. We developed comprehensive and data-based support for our position, where possible, to make clear how the business benefits from solutions that a Patient Centric approach offered. And most of all, we showed how their work would be made better from this approach.

For the most part, it's a change management adventure, because it truly impacts the way medicines can and should be developed.

Those were the early days when people weren't sure what to do with the information or how to address the recommendations. This isn't meant to be a punitive statement toward those folks who early on were confronted with this new way of working. On the contrary, innovation is always challenging at the start. Very intelligent and accomplished people often get it wrong. President Grover Cleveland believed the telephone was an interesting invention but wondered why anyone would need one. Steve Balmer – one of the founders of Microsoft – questioned the utility of the iPhone as a business tool since it had no keyboard. In the 1950's, IBM estimated the number of computers that would be bought would be in the dozens.

Why did these leaders not see the opportunities they were presented with? The clarity and certainty that is lacking in what will be successful is made up only by the dogged determination and persistent advocacy of those who believe. Many leaders, when faced with a decision filled with uncertainty, will look only to the past for guidance. While opportunity appears opaque, risk is illuminated in brilliant sunshine. To be sure, risk tolerance is not gambling. It is a measured understanding of potential. One of the key components of change management, from my perspective, is getting the right people on board that are willing to look forward, seeking innovation with a measured acceptance of risks and not looking to the safety of the rear-view mirror.

In my early years of advocating for patient centricity as a process, I met many questions around "why." Why change? Maybe it's a solution looking for a problem? The following example, which occurred more than a decade ago raised eyebrows. A researcher was working in a particular disease condition and believed in his work and the impact it would have on patients. The Patient Centricity team spoke to some patients and did an analysis which showed that the expected impact of the molecule (the science) would not be appreciably different than what was already available. This would indicate the clinically meaningful benefit to patients, beyond standard of care, was going to be minimal, and it is unlikely patients and providers (based on their feedback) would see added value in this potential product.

It seemed imprudent for us to invest in this and ultimately have little patient benefit. We had a wide open and visible disagreement, which I concluded by saying "this is your project but I'm just suggesting that this is likely not going to be something that's going to be clinically meaningful based on our analysis." Fast forward five years and the project was killed for that very reason. Five additional years of spending, five years where brilliant minds could have been focused on projects with more potential value, and most importantly, five years of time wasted for patients. All those things could have been avoided if they just simply considered more seriously the Patient Centricity inputs. It was this example that prompted the Research programs to ask that the Patient Centricity analysis become part of every review of the priority projects in the early portfolio.

The implication isn't that our analyses are always correct. They are just one part of a decision tree that includes many variables. But, while this work is not independently decisional, I do make clear that it should be evaluated and considered in decision-making. It cannot be put in a drawer and hidden just because someone doesn't like the result.

True Patient Centricity is a process where we gather information and then make it actionable, which in turn has an impact on decision-making.

Here's another early example of resistance in the frame of "we're doing this already." The senior leaders of a company were having a retreat. I was asked to present the concept of Patient Centricity and how it can impact the decisions that were made in research, development and beyond. The focus of the talk was on the recently rolled out concept of the work I had launched two and a half years earlier. The room was filled and off I went with the presentation. I covered the importance of understanding the consumer in any business as well as the impact that this understanding has had in specific industries. I then discussed what had been built to help focus the attention on the patient. When I finished, most in the room seemed quite pleased. There were a few questions on the actual processes and teams that were built to execute.

Then, a very senior leader brought up the dismal sales of a newly launched product. He said they had spoken to many patients and adjusted their work to align with the advice. "Why did we fail?" he asked. Answering his own question, he said, "the patients got it wrong." What??? Patients got it wrong? I smiled politely, paced for a few seconds in front of the group then, facing him directly asked, "Was it the patients that got it wrong or you and your teams? It is not possible for the patients to get it wrong."

Patients aren't wrong, they can't be. We are asking for their opinions. We may ask the wrong question or not ask the correct question. But what they share with us is their truth. We need to listen.

Patients have many reasons for their preferences and opinions. As we will discuss in future chapters, the environment in which they live, behaviors, age, culture, socioeconomics all play a role. Context is so important when we think about Patient Centricity. Individuals have many different priorities and responsibilities. This is very clear in the conversation we had with one young woman with rheumatoid arthritis. It reveals the complexity of the environment in which we live and the need for Pharma to move toward the patient not the other way around.

She was taking an injectable once a week. She had a young family – children in grade school – and liked to remain active, exercising regularly. We asked her if she would consider an oral agent that would be equally effective? She thought that would be great. Then we started asking her about dosing – what if this pill would have to be taken once or twice a day? She responded negatively to taking an equally effective pill once or twice a day, versus an injectable once a week. We were a bit taken aback. This was thought to be a scenario with no downside. Why? She said: "Every single day when I take that pill, it reminds me I'm a patient. I can take my injection once a week, and I can just be a mom and not a patient the rest of the week. I'm taking my kids to practice and I'm taking them to school." That would likely not be a unified perspective but if we didn't ask the right questions, we would have assumed everyone would rather take a pill. Lesson learned. Don't assume we know everything, or anything, until we actually listen.

While persistence matters in developing a Patient Centricity function, determination needs to be connected to preparation. Every day the team and I prepared for the opportunity to convince someone, to share an example, to discuss impacts. From day one we began to identify metrics that could be followed – both quantitative and qualitative. Feedback from teams we supported was always obtained in multiple formats such as post-work interviews and anonymous surveys. How this work could impact patients is clear; how it impacts the business needed to be developed and, just as importantly, followed.

The Patient Centricity process is really a change management effort. With Patient Centricity, we're changing the way medicines are developed for the first time in a very long time. However, the concept of patient involvement is being accepted because it enhances decision making and helps to align our primary goal: providing care to patients.

Pharma has a huge advantage over other industries: our people. We have a very fortunate selection bias in Pharma. If you're an accountant or human resource manager, you can work for virtually any company in the world. I believe people choose to work in Pharma, because they feel their skills can be applied to make a difference for those seeking help.

A large part of the Patient Centricity mission is to remind every team member across the organization that their work is directly contributing to the development of patient solutions. A mature Patient Centricity function is fully connected to the recruitment and retention of high performing individuals. It is the glue that connects the people to a unified corporate culture.

The broader healthcare ecosystem is ready for their evolution into a patient centric approach. It will take change agents – leaders who truly believe and are willing to meet resistance with persistence. Leaders who can create the components, show results, and never settle for anything less than what would be impactful. A process has been proposed. The time is now.

CHAPTER 3

Blindfolded and Swinging for The Fences

Patient Care And The Link To Pharma

It was what I would consider a regular week in clinical practice, seeing patients in the hospital and in the office. Many different types of visits that one would typically see in a primary care setting. Acute illnesses, follow-up visits for hypertension, cardiovascular disease, cancer, diabetes, and the occasional office procedure such as GYN exams, sutures, and the like. This day was no different. I had more than 30 patients scheduled, one of which was a young woman in her early 30's.

Linda was generally healthy and typically came into the office once or twice a year. Today she came in for her annual GYN exam. She had what most would consider a tough life, not able to attend school beyond 12th grade and she worked many different jobs to keep afloat. She was always kind, never asked for anything beyond what she should expect and never complained. Linda was fortunate to have insurance through the state Medical Assistance program.

While it wasn't equivalent to a private insurance plan, it allowed her to feel comfortable seeking and receiving care.

We had a good visit, and all seemed okay on her exam. Samples of her cervix (a Pap Smear) were sent off to the lab as is customary and a few days later I received the results. Her cervix displayed abnormal cells which needed further evaluation. She would have to get an evaluation and likely a procedure from a Gynecologist. I had my office schedule her with the large group of OB-GYN doctors in the region whom I used routinely. I had a very large primary care practice so when I say routinely, I probably used them for more than 100 referrals annually.

All seemed fine, and a few months later I saw Linda in the office. I asked how the GYN visit went as I did not have any correspondence from the gynecologist, and she said she never saw them. I was perplexed and a bit irked. Why would she not have followed up as I recommended and as my office scheduled her? Amazingly, she did follow-up but was turned away a day before the appointment. They would not see her because she had Medical Assistance as insurance. I quickly went from irked to incensed.

I immediately called the OB-GYN office myself and spoke to the office manager. The conversation was not pleasant. When I raised my concern, she responded by telling me they would only get a few dollars for that visit and that they referred her to a free clinic. I asked her what she thought I was being paid. It was less than they would be paid. We had a few more words and I ended the call telling her they would not receive another referral from me from that day forward. They did not.

Linda's story progressed with her receiving the care she needed, and all ended up well. To be fair, this is not the typical experience I have had in healthcare or even from this group of doctors. In nearly all instances, care of the patient was the priority within the network of doctors I worked with. Was this incident the fault of inexperienced staff members or the doctors themselves? I believe the responsibility ultimately falls on the doctors, but this was clearly a problem with the system.

∞ ∞ ∞

This example highlights one of many barriers patients face when accessing care. There are other individuals who have access to providers but less so to the treatments being offered. The reasons range from cost to insurance coverages and formularies and beyond. However, what strikes me most is a very basic notion: if the patient cannot receive care or treatment, the best delivery systems and drug development processes in the world are ineffective. Further, the system of care is too easily disrupted and the instant it is disrupted it is the patient that suffers. Yet the entire point of the system is for the patient. Perhaps this sounds familiar – a system built for the patient without recognizing the needs of the patient?

When I entered pharma and focused on the patient piece, I knew whatever system was created had to be durable, sustainable and if it ever broke down, the core business should be the first to feel it, stimulating correction, before the patient was impacted. That is to say, the patient centricity support system was critical to business decisions such that the business would be impacted long before the patient.

Defining Patient Centricity

In my experience no system works well if there is no common understanding or definition; a uniform thought and intention around a process. A playbook. One of the challenges across industries, and Pharma is no exception, is the use of common terms in different ways.

Early on in my Patient Centricity work I saw the term "patient engagement" used by advocacy teams, by marketing, by salespeople – all with different meaning and intention. To be very clear, engaging the patient as a consumer and as a patient are both valid in my mind. But there must be clarity as to the intention of the term. When engaging the patient as a customer, marketing teams may be asking specific questions that may help them position a product to sell. This should be executed in ways that are directly aligned with the best outcomes and options for a patient; however, the intention is, nonetheless, to sell the product. Patient Centricity engages a patient to better define patient needs, where they identify value and to seek their input broadly in developing new solutions.

Patient Centricity is and must remain brand agnostic.

So, I tried to identify that common language that would advance our call to action. Focusing on keeping it as easy as possible to understand, I developed two relatively simple components of the definition of Patient Centricity:

Operationally, it is the actionable integration of patient insights and perspectives in all decisions that impact the development of patient treatments and solutions.

Culturally, it is the conscious awareness of the patient for every employee, in every role, and in every geography, every day.

The Drug Development Process Now

To create a Patient Centricity operational process in pharma, we must recognize the strengths and limitations of the traditional drug development approach. A clear strength is a process that brings the best minds in science and clinical development together to create medicines of high medical value. It relies on scientifically driven decisions in research and statistically driven outcomes in clinical development.

However, this has often been without any true understanding of the actual perceived value delivered to our most important customer – our patients. This is akin to a professional baseball player trying to hit a baseball blindfolded. All the skills in the world, but without a key piece of information needed to bring the effort to a successful conclusion. This type of approach is rarely, if ever, seen in any other industry. Home runs – the development of new medicines well aligned with patient need and value – are rarely achieved when critical inputs are missing.

For those not familiar with the drug development process, in its most basic form, it consists of three distinct but highly complex stages:

First, there is **research**, in which scientists develop a scientific concept. A chemical entity or molecule has presumed activity and capabilities which could, in principle or by earlier study, positively impact human health. Many studies are done in a laboratory to confirm what is believed to be true: the molecule appears safe, and its behavior is as predicted. Typically, scientists present their research and results, their thinking, and their plans to other scientists within the company and to leadership. A decision is made based on these discussions as to whether the science would support further study and investment. This can consume many years of work, often the life's work of many talented scientists.

Next, there is **development**. This is a highly simplified summary of the drug development process. Many variations can and often do occur in the development of new medicines. However, for our simplified version, at this point, it is believed the research phase has proved successful and the activity of the molecular entity in fact has the potential to interact at a disease level to improve human health in some way and is likely safe. This clinical development stage of new medicine development will take years, often many years, to understand and show the potential drug impact in humans. This typically consists of three phases:

Phase 1: In which healthy subjects – minimal participants – are enrolled to determine safety of the molecular entity. Dosing information can also be obtained in this phase. Many wonder why healthy subjects? The goal in this phase is not to treat disease but to verify safety. While the molecule, through research studies, is believed to be safe and potentially effective, the only way to know for certain is clinical testing. This is best shown without additional variables that could cloud the results, for which healthy subjects are best suited.

Phase 2: These are larger studies to determine efficacy and proof-of-concept (POC); whether the entity has an impact on patients with the illness. Clear guidelines are developed for the execution of the clinical trial and all patients who enter, like Phase 1 and Phase 3, are volunteers. These studies are developed in ways to show statistical significance; that the results observed are likely not arrived at by chance. Additionally, as with all phases of clinical trials, safety is a key parameter being observed. Any trial could be stopped at any time should a safety signal arise.

Phase 3: These are often considerably larger studies to not only verify the efficacy findings observed in the smaller POC study, but to also look for any safety signals in the larger population entered into the study and being treated. These studies are typically complex and involve multiple clinical trial sites across the US or across the world.

Following the research and development phases discussed above, companies will then present their data for the entire process to regulatory bodies. The regulatory bodies (e.g.: FDA, EMA) have experts who review the information, can ask additional questions, and are tasked with deciding whether the program proved sufficiently that the new medicine is safe, effective and should be made available to patients.

Although I've described this part of the process in a simplistic way, it's important to understand that it is long and involved and requires many years and often hundreds of millions of dollars. In the research phase, most of these projects fail (more than 90%). A significant number still fail in early development, with fewer in late development.

These are high risk enterprises; even more reason to involve patients early and throughout the process. Having projects survive this arduous path but finding patients with little use for the resulting approved product is a failure of epic proportions; one that could have been avoided in many instances. This is a key component of why Patient Centricity needs to exist in every pharmaceutical and biotech company. It is essential to ensure the work being executed links to a patient's need, which then improves the likelihood that the medicines that arrive in the marketplace will contribute to clinically meaningful benefit.

The final stage is **delivery**. Once approval is obtained from regulatory agencies in each country, the medicines are manufactured and distributed across geographies and made available for providers to prescribe.

This process can also be circuitous with third parties – such as Pharmacy Benefit Managers (PBMs) – interposed between the company that develops the medicine and those that traditionally would sell directly to the patient (pharmacies). I will not dive into this layer here. **However about 50% of drugs launched in the last 15 years underperformed analysts' sales estimates by more than 20%,**[1] which demonstrates flaws in the system with a negative patient impact, business impact, and which, in my view, displays a lack of true understanding of patient need and value.

When the traditional drug development process gets underway in research, scientists with remarkable expertise would work in the lab learning and perfecting the scientific basis to what they believe could be a patient solution. This could include determining the affinity of a molecule for a receptor or its unintended effects on healthy organs.

However, these processes often lacked direct patient contact and along with that a somewhat diminished understanding of the clinical disease they were trying to treat, the patient's journey or the impacts of the current standard of care. Further, they had little, or no idea of the characteristics required of a new medicine from the perspective of patients, caregivers, or practitioners. What would constitute clinically meaningful benefit to patients and providers? Which symptom(s) is the most troublesome if a cure was not possible? These questions were either left unasked or asked but unanswered. However, they are some of the most critical questions.

Billions of dollars are being spent on these efforts to develop treatments without recognizing one basic fact: **patients do not purchase science, they purchase medicine**. And for that medicine to be useful it must satisfy the clinical needs in the context of what is already available and the diverse needs of patients across disease areas and even within a single disease area.

The Operational Element of Patient Centricity

So how do we evolve the traditional approach of very strong science and development processes? It requires new, specialized teams; teams that work in parallel of the research and developmental continuum from discovery through delivery. Patient Centricity teams bridge the gap between traditional internal project teams and patients, working closely together to produce analyses that include patient insights but also more traditional pieces of information to allow for enhanced decision-making.

The Patient Centricity model is essentially a parallel work stream that continually dips into the traditional processes. It provides critical information from patients that integrates need, value, and preferences into all decision-points. How does this influence decisions? It creates open and obvious points of discussion that had been previously absent: What does the patient think? What do they expect from this new solution? What is the provider perspective? What does the caregiver think? How does the standard of care fall short?

The result of these interactions is remarkable. Project teams in research ask probing questions when presented with patient expectations. They discuss more deeply the potential impact of their science and consider whether the effort could be successful from both a patient and provider perspective.

It is no longer a discussion among scientists about the science alone. Instead, it is an expanded discussion about how the science links to clinical expectations. We have moved from simply pushing forward with an idea to one linking the science to the patient population where the impact will match need. The result of these discussions will influence where investments are made, which projects are promoted, and where human resources are committed. Put simply: Patient Centricity, engaging actively with internal partners, is an essential component to any drug development process. To not have this as a mature function will create a disadvantage among competitors in the future.

Most importantly, every one of us should have an expectation that this process will be adopted across Pharma. Who among us will not be a patient at some point or care for someone who is? How do we achieve our future expectations of health and care if we continue to work in ways that leave out key pieces of information necessary to develop future solutions that are of high value to the end user? Research and development are costly. We need to concentrate our efforts where they will yield the greatest benefit, and this cannot be done without collaborating with patients. And for those balance sheet focused readers – it's good business.

Wasted resources – human and financial – defeat our aligned goals of developing clinically meaningful solutions in the most time efficient manner. This is not a primer of an interesting new function; it is a call to action for each of us to make clear anything less than full implementation is unacceptable.

CHAPTER 4

This Bandana Is All I Have

Patient Barriers To Care And Their Real-World Experiences

Stephen was in his 60's and was a quiet but friendly man. I only met him by chance; he would come to the office when his girlfriend, Martha, had appointments. Both were wonderful people and together they meshed very well. Stephen was a Vietnam War combat veteran and each time we spoke nearly every sentence he uttered ended with a respectful "sir." I always enjoyed catching up with them.

Stephen didn't come to every appointment with Martha, so it didn't really occur to me that I hadn't seen him in a while. As months passed, Martha arrived for one of her regularly scheduled appointments and she was visibly upset. Apparently, Stephen had not been feeling well for many weeks but would not seek medical care. She told me that he had called a local VA Hospital and was awaiting his appointment. He had a bad experience at a VA Hospital in the past and was very hesitant to go back into that system. He would not schedule with any other doctors because of his lack of insurance. He simply couldn't afford a visit and refused to accept care without paying. Martha and I chatted for a while and because I knew Stephen a bit, I asked her to invite him to see me that week. Amazingly, he agreed, and we met in the office two days later.

When I walked into the exam room it was clear Stephen was quite ill. He sat on the exam table slouched. He raised his head and eyes to the door when I walked in but there was no other movement. I don't recall him saying anything when I entered. He was wearing a worn-out blue T-shirt and an old pair of jeans. He hadn't shaved in some time, but his scruff couldn't hide the clear and pronounced jawline made more prominent by his significant weight loss. He had gotten so thin that you could see the beating of his carotid arteries in his neck. When I greeted him and shook his hand, his grip was weak, his voice low and hoarse. He winced when he spoke, indicating it was painful. His blue eyes told the story – worn and sad, his stare interrupted with very slow blinks.

I asked Stephen some questions about his illness, getting as much history as I could, being very conscious of his discomfort with speaking. When I examined him, I suspected he had throat cancer. I discussed the potential seriousness of this with Stephen and the importance of him seeing a specialist as soon as possible. Despite the news, I got the sense it was no surprise to him. Perhaps he didn't know specifically what was wrong, but he was very sure it was serious.

I scheduled him with an Ear, Nose and Throat (ENT) doctor who was a friend, and then back to see me in a week. He politely refused the follow-up stating he could not pay me, and he didn't expect me to work for free. This was important to him, having worked hard all his life, he was not about to start asking for "handouts." At that moment, the conversation I had with my father at Starbucks, mentioned earlier in the Forward, flashed through my mind. I simply refused to accept that answer. I politely but firmly told Stephen it was my choice, how I spent my time, how I ran my office, and he should follow-up as recommended.

With that conversation behind us, weeks passed, and multiple visits took place with me and with the ENT doctor. He underwent a surgical resection of his cancer and a few weeks post-op he came to an appointment in the office, still weak and thin, as he sat on the exam table. He had with him a small white cardboard box. When the exam was completed, he said to me: "Doc, I can't thank you enough for your willingness to care for me. I don't know what I would have done. I don't have much in this world but the one thing that I do have – what means the most to me - is this," as he handed me the box.

Inside was a cleaned and perfectly folded black bandana with multiple colored military insignias on it. Through tears he said, "I wore this every day in Vietnam and feel like it kept me safe. It's all I have that really matters to me and I want you to have it." I was speechless. After a long pause and holding back a few tears myself, I told him I couldn't accept it. He insisted, "please take it. I am sure you are the one who should have it."

∞ ∞ ∞

I often reflect on my relationship with Stephen. There is so much in that interaction to unwrap. It addresses flaws in the delivery system, of course. The fact that care has many layers and the two most obvious barriers that can exist are access to the care delivery system and access to treatment – the actual medicine. The first barrier is what Stephen experienced. Whether self-imposed or not, he did not have access to the "treaters" in the delivery system and as a result, he lacked care. Others may have access to the delivery system but not the medicines themselves. This could be due to financial limitations, lack of insurance, formulary restrictions or geography. Some individuals have limited access to both. Here we can define, broadly, the trifecta of potential barriers that we need to consider if care is the primary objective of the collective "healthcare system":

1) Are the medicines that are being produced clinically meaningful to patients?
2) Do patients have access to the delivery system?
3) If access is obtained, can they secure the clinically meaningful treatments?

Even a superficial analysis of these issues points out clearly that it is not a single system problem. It involves drug developers, healthcare providers and the broader healthcare ecosystem that includes governments and payers. My work has been primarily on the delivery and pharma side and these exposures have made clear to me that solving for one in a disjointed way solves very little.

These systems need to communicate; there needs to be awareness of all perspectives to drive solutions out of a board room and into every exam room. As I developed Patient Centricity functions within Pharma, I went to great lengths to bring the exam room into the research labs. That connectivity is so important as scientists begin to think about the potential of the science. To be certain that what is expected in the delivery system should be transparent to the scientists – hopefully encouraging serious discussions around scientific potential from a patient and healthcare provider perspective. This linkage allows us to solve the first of the issues noted – increasing the likelihood that what is produced will, in fact, solve a much-needed gap in care. This work also alerts our teams to any delivery issues that may occur in the "real-world."

To those who are skeptical, I fully agree the other two issues are not likely to be solved by Pharma alone. They are complex and vary greatly by geography – even by zip code. However, does pharma have an interest in these challenges being addressed? Absolutely. The best medicine is merely interesting science until it is utilized by a patient and has the desired result.

Patient Centricity is not a siloed concept. It is an enterprise function that sees success in the partnerships with patients throughout the process of drug development through to successful treatment delivery. If we fail at any point, Patient Centricity fails. I do believe that Patient Centricity capabilities within each of the enterprise's components will be the point of communication and solution development. The formula doesn't need to change much; it's about addressing culture and evolving operations to align firmly with patient needs. It may sound familiar because it is a common theme I come back to in this book.

Stephen's story also shines a light on the differences in the environments in which we live, our individual perspectives. His context was quite different to my own experiences and those of the patients I saw for the rest of that day. As I've written before, our job at its essence – whether pharma or healthcare delivery – is to provide care for people. To do that, we need to understand them in their real-world setting. How they perceive the environment, their own challenges and how they approach their version of a solution. Despite his illness, his pride in fending for himself was his priority. His hesitancy to enter a system that appeared to him to be more retail in nature was front and center. Stephen's life experiences were dramatic in many ways and his evolution within those experiences unique to him. If we don't recognize that, if we simply dismiss it as too difficult to factor in, then we are missing a critical piece to effectively treat patients. We need also to become more discerning as to whether our healthcare systems are designed to accept these learnings, evolve, and begin the process of attempting to leave no one behind.

Understanding the Real-World Experience of Patients

Patients are not a monolithic group, and we should never treat them as such. Creating solutions for patients can only be achieved on a broad scale when we have knowledge of their real-world experiences, their potential limitations and challenges in their own environment, and their unique needs. All components of the healthcare development and delivery system should have this information baked into their processes early and often to be sure the solution available fits the needs of patients not just in one environment, but many.

The skeptics will argue that any system built to treat large populations cannot effectively be personalized. That is true. However, when we acknowledge the uniqueness of every patient it should not be at the expense of their commonalities. Even the skeptics would have to admit that we have not evolved most systems in a patient centric way to address the shortcomings in the commonality category. One last point on this, if we address the important challenges impacting most patients, it will take only minor tweaks, often at the point of contact, to address the more personalized requests and needs of individuals. This is explained, through example, in later chapters.

The rigidity of current systems also creates a propensity for them to break suddenly when under pressure. Flexibility in system design, the ability to learn and evolve, will allow processes to evolve more quickly and deliver services more consistently for the people they are designed to serve.

Within the Pharma space, obtaining patient insights in the real-world setting is essential to deliver solutions that are meaningful. The differences across geographies, socioeconomic levels, and cultural variables all impact our ability to do so. It also impacts the patient's perception of value and their willingness to accept treatment.

For example, in some regions of the world screening for prostate cancer is not accepted readily for fear, if found, of impotence from treatment. This presents a layer of understanding and planning that is essential if we are to make meaningful treatments available in such settings. Certainly, this is not a Pharma issue alone; it involves the broader healthcare ecosystem as well. But that is the point – it starts with developing the solution with an eye toward the environments where it can be utilized while simultaneously recognizing our downstream partners' aligned efforts in delivering those solutions. We need mechanisms to successfully connect the first mile and last mile portions of the development and delivery road to successfully care for the person.

In a mature Patient Centricity function in Pharma, connecting meaningful science, patient need, and value to the delivery system is essential. A Patient Insights team, whose entire focus is on the patient "where they live" provides this bridge between drug developer and delivery systems. (see appendix A).

While patients live their lives in varying environments, one thing is certain, the clinical trial setting in which therapies are evaluated in humans is very dissimilar to any of those environments. Trial sites have the vials and equipment that sponsors provide, and the patient returns at set intervals at which time the trial personnel document all the details of each patients' condition. Their compliance and adherence to the protocol is monitored closely. Upon regulatory approval, the Pharma dilemma is how to deliver the medicine successfully in an environment that is nothing like the trial environment we created and within which we have thus far interacted with patients. So how do pharmaceutical companies create the capabilities to understand all these complexities?

The bridge to those two very different worlds **is** Patient Centricity.

Siloes, A Nudge and A Lot of Collaboration

This idea of Patient Centricity first began with a focus on how medicines are developed. Connecting patients to the process. However, along my journey I realized delivery of those medicines will require more. Having been privileged to gain exposure in my career to different areas of the healthcare ecosystem, the importance of close interaction between the development and delivery systems struck me. Accessing care but not having clinically meaningful treatments available or having available treatments but no access to care is a complete and utter failure. This siloed and disconnected approach needs to be retired permanently. The future of quality care will require an enterprise approach among developers and delivery systems. It will require careful navigation down The Path to a Patient Centric Healthcare System.

Is this unchartered territory? The Lewis and Clark work of healthcare? Absolutely not. To add a bit of broader context, there are few if any companies in other industries that would develop a product if they didn't understand the end users' intent, access, and usefulness of impact. Imagine this scenario: a wearable tech company produces a 10-pound necklace to track activity; the scientists working on it believe data capture is better with this device. Commercial folks aren't sure of the value, but this is what they were handed. Lemons to lemonade, right? Have they balanced the technical capabilities with customer expectations to be sure the solution achieves the goals necessary but also satisfies customer needs? After all, the customer will need to agree to wear it for it to be useful. An exaggerated story but you get my point.

Successful organizations determine what would be useful to the customer – where the customer lives – and then determine how best to create access to their products. It's a linkage that is unbreakable if a product is to be successful and the customer is to benefit from the innovation. This seems logical yet, in healthcare, we don't yet have this firm linkage between the development of new solutions and the delivery system, the connection of treatment availability and care delivery.

Does Pharma sometimes have an R&D proce
a product that is passed to commercial – th
example – without fully factoring in its use and
Unfortunately, if being honest, the answer is yes. As an industry we have developed great science and linked it to a disease, but we have not consistently made the effort to fully understand what patients wanted. How patients could benefit from it.

Pharma needs to better understand how patients view efficacy improvements over standard of care, symptoms that are most problematic not currently being addressed, their interaction with healthcare providers, and their interaction with healthcare systems for such things as diagnosis, testing, and treatment delivery. Even if we can't control it, we need to break down the silos and start to work with these other components of the system.

If our goal is to deliver care for a patient, it is not reasonable to say "well, our part's done, and I hope that the other people fix their part." It's incumbent upon the systems to understand the patient in all aspects. To nudge each other and work together to change the approach.

Scientific advancement has been incredible, but how many patients are still being left behind? How many medicines have been produced but underperform because patients and providers don't find them useful? How many patients don't have access? How many patients have not been educated to understand that treatment is available? How many exam room conversations are missed, because either the patient does not bring up the ɔblem or the doctor does not ask the question? All these challenges can begin to be addressed across organizations with a dedicated Patient Centricity function involved.

Stephen's story motivates us to recognize that patients are diverse and have very different challenges. That the systems constructed may not be perfect and deserve study. Most importantly, we should accept that acknowledging system shortcomings is not a projection of blame or intent. It is simply a way forward, a method to start the discussion. Perhaps I've made a few folks angry with the assertions I've made. That's not my intention but it's ok if it begins dialogue. I'm sure many are nodding in agreement, because like me, they are part of a system they wish was a bit better. Having been part of the many systems I've discussed here; I share as much blame as anyone.

My observations and suggestions are not intended to project certainty of solution but instead certainty of method. There is no question in my mind that a Patient Centricity function in each organization across the ecosystem will begin the path to a solution. How can it not be of benefit? We are involving the very customers that will utilize all our "products." Let's not approach this with hubris but with humility. We can do better – all of us.

When I think back to Stephen, I am so appreciative of the lesson he provided me. Occasionally, I'll look at that bandana. Holding it, I wonder what he felt like when he wore it, his future so uncertain. His fear. He shared with me a piece of his life in such a generous way. Thank you, sir.

CHAPTER 5

A Bluebird in The Sun

Behavior And How It Impacts Care

Carol was a soft-spoken woman in her 70's. Small in stature and very kind, she lived alone having never been married. Her support network was her sister and a few friends. She arrived at the clinic at the hospital where I was a 3rd year resident, having been referred by someone else I cared for. She had a pleasant soft smile on her face when she entered the exam room. Her demeanor was one that made anyone in her presence comfortable. She chose to sit on the exam table not the chair near my stool and did so with energy, using her arms to "jump" onto the table with ease. She swung her feet back and forth as we talked.

Did the physical distance in the exam room mirror her hesitance to be there, I wondered? Carol generally felt well yet was quite nervous; she was not a frequent visitor to doctors and was fearful of the healthcare system. She spoke quickly but in a soft voice. During our discussion, with deep probing, it became clear she was having some shortness of breath with activity over the last couple of months. She didn't say so, but I suspected this was probably observed by her sister and prompted the recommendation for a checkup.

On exam she had a significant murmur consistent with Aortic Stenosis – a narrowing of the valve at the opening connecting the left ventricle to the aorta. This can be serious and could require surgical correction if severe. I talked to Carol about this, and she became quite anxious.

"I'm fine doctor. I don't need anything done," she said.

I explained to her in detail the possible issue and that it was fixable. But I also told her that a non-invasive study would initially be needed to confirm the diagnosis. She finally agreed. We talked for quite a long time at that first visit about her anxieties and her life. It was then that Carol told me about her volunteer activities and the glass bluebirds she made. She gave these to people in her life and explained to me that they should sit in sunlight; on a shelf or sill near a window, and they will bring blessings and love to those in the home. When she spoke of the bluebirds she seemed to relax and smile more often. She was in her comfort zone.

Within the week Carol had the echocardiogram, and it did reveal severe aortic stenosis. We had another long discussion and I explained to her she would need to see a cardiologist and likely would require surgery. She was in a panic again, initially refusing any further referrals or treatment.

"I can't do it, doctor. I think I'll be ok" she said, her voice faint and shaking. Again, we talked through it, and she left the visit agreeable to see the cardiologist. We spoke very frequently by phone in the next week; she would call me when she was very anxious, and we would work through it together. She saw the cardiologist and then the surgeon and despite some delays due to her refusing to move forward because of her anxiety, she was scheduled for surgery. Again, multiple calls and discussions with Carol occurred – she was extremely anxious about the surgery and often told me she wanted to cancel the procedure only to be convinced it was necessary.

The night before the surgery I was on call at the hospital and Carol phoned me very late into the night. She didn't want to have the surgery and was considering cancelling. We talked for quite some time and she, once again, agreed to the plan. In fact, the hour was quite late, and she was due to be at the hospital in six hours. I told her I would be there to greet her when she arrived. I worked through the night and received a call from the ER – Carol must have just arrived for her procedure, I thought. Not so. Instead, it was the ER doc informing me Carol had died.

I was shocked and quite sad. When I spoke with her a few hours before, we ended the call with her laughing and less anxious.

Two weeks later I was in the clinic seeing patients and the receptionists told me someone was there to see me. Between patients I had them bring the individual to a room. It was Carol's sister. She was so kind, thanking me for the care I provided and letting me know how much Carol appreciated me. It was humbling and, if I'm being honest, quite uncomfortable. It made me feel even less adequate with the outcome.

She handed me a small box – about the size that would hold a ring. She said "Carol had this put aside for weeks. She made it for you and your family and was planning to give it to you the morning of her procedure." Inside was a bluebird with a kind note attached. Sky blue in color, the light seemed to pass through and reflect off of it at the same time.

I sat holding the bluebird for at least a minute, finding it difficult to muster up something to say. I was very thankful and a bit frustrated that things didn't end the way we all had hoped. But I didn't sense that from Carol's sister. She sat close to me with a kind half smile on her face. I remember thinking after the visit that her sister seemed to feel Carol in the room with us at that moment. I did as well.

∞ ∞ ∞

The point of this story of the bluebird – and its relation to Patient Centricity – is that all patients have their own internal processing mechanism. Clearly, understanding that is both complex and challenging. I was a resident, on-call and working all night when Carol called me that evening at 11:30. I was awake and had the time to spend with her. The reality of a provider in practice today, likely seeing 30 people or more a day, it is questionable how much of that interaction could have happened as it had. Since my clinical practice days, the system has grown more obtuse; more institutionalized.

When you institutionalize care – such as hospitalists (which I do not oppose) – there are trade-offs. On the side of improvement is expert care available, often 24/7, in person and at the bedside. These individuals can provide regular and critical care at a moment's notice where often, in the past, the primary doctor would have been outside the hospital and either phoning in orders or arriving sometime later. However, what is compromised is an understanding of context – your life, your support network, your fears. They can lack a deep understanding that the primary physicians had due to multiple visits and relationships established. This may not sacrifice the appropriate treatment but does, in some ways, impact the level of care received. This is discussed in more detail in Chapter 9. As we continue to advance in this direction in healthcare, I am concerned care is at risk of worsening unless changes are instituted.

Carol's story is not unique. It is being repeated across the country every single day. We need to allocate more time to listen. Understanding the complexity of that individual patient can't be done if it's institutionalized. It is impossible. Carol was someone who had every good trait that would benefit those around her, but not herself. She was just so anxious about her care and what could happen. This slowed the process down. And ultimately, that extra day, extra week, extra month mattered. Even with more time, as in the case with Carol, all patients will not be perfectly served, but many more will.

But the point isn't that Carol took 24 hours too long in her process. Every day patients enter the system with their own barriers to care that could be chipped away given sufficient time for discussion. There is significant value in time spent in bidirectional communication – listening to the challenges while educating the patient regarding the disease, the treatment as well as the benefit/risks. This is where I think most practitioners would agree – if they only had the time, there would be nothing more important and fulfilling than to spend time on this type of communication. However, the system they are in is often inflexible. More doctors are part of employed healthcare systems with fewer being in private practice. Even those in private practices are under enormous pressure to do more with less time and often fewer resources.

With all these issues Carol brings us, what can we do? What is a simplified approach to this complex situation? We need to develop and deliver new medicines effectively with a better understanding of behavior.

Many studies have been done over the years linking behavior to healthcare outcomes – some say there is a 50% association between behavior and outcomes, some more. But getting lost in the percentages obscures the point: behavior matters.

Carol resisted interactions with the healthcare system. She came for a check-up at the insistence of her sister and even then, was hesitant to share any symptoms. Her disease was very advanced. If we are to present these individuals with solutions as a Pharma company, we need to understand the different barriers they face. Carol was one example; there are many others from both sides of the examination table. Conversations that are critical but avoided by patients or missed by practitioners – a result of short visits and no extra time for discussion. How can we expand the variables considered by Pharma and the healthcare delivery system to include patient behavior? Patient Centricity is the platform for this.

This information is also important in understanding the types of solutions that will work in the real world.

The creation of a specialized behavioral capability has allowed for teams within Pharma to ask pertinent questions before solutions are fully developed and delivered, for patients and patient groups to raise important aspects of care from their perspective, and for issues to be studied and solutions developed prior to the launch of a new medicine. How can we solve for such issues as influenza vaccination in pregnant women if we don't understand the complex dynamic between the patient and the provider? The socioeconomic and cultural differences of the patients we intend to treat? The patient will not be offered a potential solution or preventative therapy if neither the patient nor the provider raises the subject in the exam room. A lack of understanding of the patient's circumstances may provide them with a prescription, but the inability to have it filled due to cost. This will not offer any benefit. The behavioral science aspect to Patient Centricity is a critical component without which a fully patient centric system cannot be realized.

Additionally, from an organizational perspective, behavioral expertise can be deployed internally to allow for transitions and transformations to occur more smoothly while maintaining a customer centric understanding and approach. This is applicable across industries and businesses. We have deployed this expertise successfully in helping teams approach changes in process and workstreams as well as downsizing and high stress transformations with more positivity and energy. Understanding the individual worker, the patient, and our own leadership weaknesses and strengths is essential for successful organizational evolution.

This is a critical point: systems will not evolve if we as leaders are not open to hearing the good, the bad, and the ugly. Not all input requires action but, unfortunately, input is often acknowledged but decidedly filed away in the to-do category. Understanding our own behavior can help change this approach creating a default toward action when deemed reasonable.

Behavioral understanding when the capability exists within organizations is not abstract or vague. Specific questions can be researched and addressed efficiently. Over the years, my teams have addressed questions around adherence and compliance in specific disease areas and within patient demographics, topical conversations that may not be happening regularly during check-up exams and cultural biases in different regions of the world. These learnings can be supplemented with a vast amount of published literature and information readily available that can be actionable in short order – many times in weeks, not months or years. These are learnings that can be applied to both organizational activity and patient education.

On the delivery side, what would it take to help the Carols that enter our systems a few times a week? I would say not much. While most physicians will not have the availability to spend the overnight hours in conversation with a patient, we can spend 10 minutes more each day in the hospital. Perhaps spending some of the extra minutes discussing the non-medical aspects of care. Hospital CEOs are now mumbling "I thought this guy was a clinician at one point. An administrator. He talks like he has no idea of how this is done and what works." Maybe I am a bit off-kilter, but I don't think so. If you would, go up a few paragraphs and read the behavior section and "the good, the bad and the ugly" sentence. Maybe I'm not so crazy and perhaps the cost of those 10 minutes per person hospitalized is well worth the additional hospitalist? My ask here is not that you accept my premise but to not reject it out of hand. Simply consider it, discuss it with your teams and determine if there is a bit of sanity in what I have proposed as it relates to the work you do.

Reason will lead us to the same place: it all depends on what we measure for success. Balance sheet alone or balance sheet and outcomes. Medical outcomes and satisfaction scores. Good medical outcomes with emotional bruises all over the patients and caregivers after surviving the battlefield of hospitalization is not an optimal outcome. This is discussed more in later chapters and speaks to a cultural evolution within organizations allowing them to listen and develop more patient centric systems of care. I believe the cost is not material if culture is the platform for change and metrics are expanded to account for not only "what" was delivered but also "how" it was delivered.

When we consider change and addressing the individual, as I have written earlier, it need not be drastic to have an impact; it needs to be patient focused.

Simple examples of how a heightened awareness of the patient's experience can have an impact. When I was making rounds, it would bother me when someone – medical staff, housekeeping, whomever – would walk into a patient's room to do whatever they needed to do without knocking or respectfully addressing the patient. That's not the right attitude to help build the bridge for the patient and help to make their experience a bit more pleasant. When a patient occupies a hospital room it should be treated like their private space. You wouldn't barge into someone's home, nor should you do so in their hospital room. A simple knock on the door, announcing who you are and what you are there to do goes a long way. These oversights are not intentional; we tend to assume, during a busy day doing important work, that the smaller things are less relevant to people with bigger concerns. I would argue it's additive; yes, less of a critical issue but lowers one's tolerance for dealing with additional less critical issues. It's an aggravation multiplier, and disrespectful of another human.

On the same rounds I've experienced care being deli remarkably tender way. In the Gastro-Intestinal lab p sedation for a colonoscopy I've heard the nurse and anesthetist softly explain every step, reassuring the patient with both their words and touch that they would take good care of them. "Close your eyes and try to relax. All is okay. When you wake up, you'll be in recovery." This costs nothing. It's patient centric. And it's good business.

Today, that bluebird still sits on a shelf near a window in my home emphasizing the sunlight and reminding me of Carol and the lesson she taught me: patients are individuals and have their own set of fears and anxieties; their own strengths and weaknesses. Quiet or loud, shy or outgoing, we all have a unique story to tell. A story that should be heard and considered deeply – especially in the healthcare setting. What may be simple and easy for one patient may be difficult and dreaded by another. Our beliefs and behaviors need to be recognized and accounted for in the way we approach the creation and delivery of services. One size does not fit all.

CHAPTER 6

The Patient as A Disruptor

Evolution vs. Extinction

"An organization's ability to learn, and translate that learning into action rapidly, is the ultimate competitive advantage."

– Jack Welch

I have been in the Patient Centricity space for more than a decade – long before Patient Centricity was a term and patient engagement was a widespread topic of conversation. Over the ensuing years it was apparent any movement toward a more patient-focused process within Pharma was going to require us to challenge conventional thinking while developing a business rationale for change.

I knew this was not going to be an easy task; we are dealing with highly intelligent, driven people who are experts in their respective fields. They have confidence in current methods of delivery for patients and are not easily moved. Georg Christoph

Lichtenberg, an 18th century German scientist, once said "We accumulate our opinions at an age where are understanding is the weakest." The point: opinions are hard to change. We should accept that the path to a patient centric healthcare system will not be well lit and easily navigated. It will require disruption and a business approach if we are to convince decision-makers that this change is critical to the future of medicine development and delivery.

Disruptive innovation is a term coined by Professor Clayton Christianson in his 1997 book, *The Innovator's Dilemma*. Disruptive innovation is often misunderstood as something that disrupts current processes in a chaotic way. Throughout my career I've often heard individuals suggest they were being "a disruptor" when they utilized a different approach to address a problem that didn't work but did create a chaotic response. That misses the mark. True disruptive innovation is a new service or product line entering a market at a foundational level, gaining market share, and moving up the chain to "disrupt" more established services or products in that market. Basically, it is a new idea that grows in its ability to change a market and establish a new best-in-class approach and/or product.

We have seen this over the years with well-established businesses. Two well-known examples are Amazon versus other retailers and Netflix competing with Blockbuster. Both Amazon and Netflix started by competing at a basic level: Amazon as a seller of only books, and Netflix with a movie-by-mail format. Soon enough, Amazon established a business that was competing (and winning) against nearly all retailers. Meanwhile, Blockbuster has one remaining store in the US while Netflix evolved into streaming and digital services and announced in late 2022 a nearly $1Billion investment in a production studio in New Jersey.

Why is this relevant? I believe Patient Centricity is the next disruptor in drug development. It began nearly a decade ago with patient engagement activities, meeting patients and hearing their perspectives on their disease, treatment options, and their journey. While patient engagement was, and remains, a crucial component within Patient Centricity processes, it falls short of connecting information to action. It did, however, provide one key step along our path – it became accepted that engaging the patient is an important part of new drug development.

However, the full integration of the patient perspective into solution development that connects information to action, something rare even today, will change the way companies prioritize molecules in research and decide early on whether a potential intervention has value in the eyes of patients, caregivers, and providers.

Engaging the customer is not a new concept in and of itself. In fact, most industries engage their customers long before the first product is mass produced. From the complexity of a car's electronic interfaces to the simplicity of a handheld razor, customers are asked to provide feedback on real world use. Adjustments in the products are made or they are entirely dropped based on the feedback. In every instance, this customer interaction is designed for one purpose: to be certain what is produced satisfies a need or preference. Are medicines immune from such considerations?

As mentioned earlier, an L.E.K. consulting study about the launch of new medicines found that nearly 50% of drugs launched in the last 15 years underperformed analysts' sales estimates by more than 20%.[2]

Most industries believe, or want to believe, there will be high acceptance for their new products. Companies put great effort into the complex calculations that attempt to foreshadow product uptake by customers; all based on the belief that customers will see value in what is being offered. Analysts review these projections and make their own assessments regarding market consumption. Expectations of the company and the analysts will be revised when real-time data can be assessed. However, the quality of the original projections does matter, because when they are projecting, they are doing so, in part, based on what they believe the consumer's response will be to it.

When we consider the significant number of medicines that fail to meet market expectations – that's not just a real shortfall, it's a failure. Pharma may ask: Why? In truth, we know why. Because something was produced that while scientifically sound, doesn't have a clinically meaningful benefit for the patient, healthcare provider, or caregiver perspective. Maybe from all three perspectives.

Said another way, medicines were developed that didn't meet

the basic needs of the patients they were meant to treat. This is the worst outcome in my view – more disappointing than development processes that fail outright. Here you have a full development plan, all-in financial investment, a regulatory approval that yields a medicine or treatment that ends up sitting on a shelf. Large sums of money spent, as well as the ability of scientists and development folks that could have been deployed to more viable programs aligned with patient expectations. Worst of all is the loss of time – the irreplaceable commodity for us all – especially those waiting for treatment options.

Why does this shortfall happen? Well, there are likely multiple reasons, but, again, one for certain is the lack of direct patient insights integrated into the process early enough. If it was clear early on that what the product is likely to deliver will fall far short of expectations – or lack improvement over currently available treatment options, would the investment have been made to produce it? I hope we can all agree that the resounding answer is NO! This is the business argument for Patient Centricity. In future chapters (and appendices), my intention is to show both the important elements of Patient Centricity, how to create them, and discuss what they can potentially achieve. They might be somewhat different in execution for different companies, but the fundamentals remain quite consistent.

Corporate Reputation Also Matters

Patient Centricity is not only valuable from a business standpoint, but also from a reputational perspective. In a 2023 WE Brands In Motion Health Study[3] they noted that prescribers value corporate reputation. Beyond efficacy and safety, corporate reputation is the number one influencing factor in prescribing decisions and is even more influential than a healthcare professional's relationship with their sales representative. And, in fact, patient centricity is the Number One trait or behavior that those surveyed are looking for in a pharma company.

It is unfortunate but an undeniable fact that Pharma's reputation currently is not great. According to Gallup Research,[4] Pharma has the worst positivity rating of US Business and Industry Ratings by the public. The healthcare industry in general isn't too much better off reputationally, but Pharma's is lower than the United States government, and that's saying a lot. The oil and gas industry and the banking industry have better reputations than Pharma.

We can debate the reasons for this, but I believe it goes beyond the public discussions of drug prices. Clearly, this is an industry not shy about its commitment to developing new therapies for patients in need, as pharmaceutical research, and development expenditures more than quadrupled (to $102B) between 1999 and

2021.[5] I don't see this as a rebuke of the workforce either. "Our" people are truly inspired; working each day to provide benefit to others. Having worked in the healthcare delivery and Pharma space for my entire career I can say without question, I have been privileged to do so.

I believe much of it stems from our perceived disconnect with the very people we are here to serve. We need to proactively engage and collaborate, building solutions together, traveling this long path of development and delivery in a more transparent way. Much of the disconnect is because we have for too long worked behind a one-way mirror peeking into the lives of patients when we felt the need and having patients see only their reflection. Patient Centricity will shatter the mirror and create a great open space for communication.

The truth is that cost of drugs will always be a sticky issue, but whatever price we arrive at, if real value is absent, it's all the worse. If the value to the patient is present, most people would agree it's a good place to begin the discussion. The starting point should be about how we develop medicines for patients, with patients. Value is our common destination.

How Do We Get There: Disruption

Disruptive innovation typically does not happen spontaneously. We cannot expect that by merely discussing the importance of the patient, things will rapidly unfold for the better. Instead, expect a certain amount of resistance; change is rarely easy. To create change, you need to be clear about why and how this issue will be addressed. It requires a business approach and mindset.

When I was first leaning into this topic more than 14 years ago, some people were quite interested in the concept, but others were highly dismissive. "How can patients possibly be involved in research," researchers were wondering. "I've worked most of my life on this, and now you're going to add complexity that is undefinable into the decision making?" "What if I don't like what you say, or what the result is?"

I adopted a "Head, Heart, Hands" approach. First, the Head – how do we convince people logically that it makes sense? Then the Heart – how do we get them to believe in it, not just understand it intellectually? Finally, the Hands – how do we get them to act on it?

As I noted in Chapter Two, I looked at this as dealing with a bell curve. 2.5% of the people love innovation; basically, they'll say "yes" to any new idea that seems reasonable. Then, there's 2.5% who refuse to change at all; they hate change, they don't want any change, and particularly if it's not their idea. Then there's the 95% in the middle, who just want to do a better job and are less concerned with change in and of itself or the politics associated with it. This middle majority will accept an idea if you can show them, by example, that it helps them in their execution.

The initial challenge for us was how to best disrupt to bring on the "early adopters" and confirm for them that Patient Centricity in drug development was the real deal. Then it was a question of highlighting the successes – sharing examples – to convince the majority of the value for them in their work. As I have written, we addressed the "never changers" but did not obsess over their conversion; always interacting with them respectfully, listening to them, but ultimately viewing it as a yield and not a stop sign. Eventually, most of the people seeing value in the work and collaborative effort creates an outlier feeling of being left behind and that will typically pull a good portion of that 2.5% into the fold. That's the approach I've taken.

Convincing the first few folks in the early days made me feel more like a "pitchman" than a doctor. I went up to Cambridge with an early team member or two and visited with research team after research team, much like selling cookies door to door – knocking on the door of every project leader I could find. Most teams weren't interested in what we had to offer. Then, when one team finally said "Okay, we'll work with you on an analysis and see the value it offers," I knew we had our chance. I was confident I could transform that "yes" – their intellectual acceptance of the potential value of the work - into their belief. Their Heart. After that first analysis, that team not only believed but evangelized the work. They quickly moved into actively using the Patient Centricity input for all their work – the Hands. That's really all it took. Within 6 months we had global teams asking for support.

Then my role became one to ensure that if we were providing this, they couldn't just slip it into a drawer if they didn't like the result of the input. It didn't mean they had to accept our conclusions, but it did mean they had to consider them. That was the rule. And it was accepted.

What Does Success Look Like? Hard Work

While the above reveals the method of establishing a Patient Centricity function within an organization; it's no leisurely stroll. There's quite a bit of heavy lifting involved. Successful integration of the patient perspective requires established teams and specific measurable processes. Creating a culture focused on the patient, within each company, will be critical for sustainability. You need to get leadership on board – not as passive observers but creators of momentum.

I think right now most senior leaders are at the "Head" stage and I have heard from colleagues across companies that they have had a difficult time getting them to truly believe. They have found it challenging to get into the "Heart" of the leaders in such a way that Patient Centricity is viewed in equal importance to the business functions that they've become comfortable with for many years. I have been fortunate to be surrounded by leaders who truly believe in the Patient Centric drug development model. They may have been unsure as to how to execute – the hands – but their heart was all in and much of the success achieved would not have been possible without that support.

To be sure, the way from the head to the hands is a long, torturous path. As leaders within the patient centricity functions feel the pressure they can begin to compromise on their goals because to them it becomes an existential threat; the very existence of the function feels at risk. The result is a higher barrier created to capturing the hearts of everyone else, because it has been compromised and no longer has the intended impact.

The Patient Centricity function will need to parallel the entire drug development process. Every single stage that exists in the traditional drug process – from research through development and delivery – has a stage where patient centricity input should be considered. Every step is informed by the patient so that early on we can decide whether the science being considered can be reasonably expected to have a clinically meaningful impact, taking into consideration emerging standard of care, patient need and perceived value as well as HCP and caregiver perspectives.

Some may argue that engaging the patient can and should wait until later in the process. There is so much wrong with this approach. Later in the process, there have been significant investments made, plenty of sunk costs and less incentive to stop a program that could yield little benefit to patients. Additionally, once a project is far advanced, the interaction with the patient is
·om a consumer perspective not a collaborator perspective.
ıs aren't altered; instead, past decisions are informed. We

need to partner with patients to change how medicines are developed by altering the way we make decisions early and how we intend to deliver innovative solutions.

Evolution vs. Extinction

The leadership piece is often a barrier when I speak to my colleagues within Pharma and other industries that are "disrupting." All change involves effort and risk. Understanding the risk tolerance of ourselves and other leaders in our organizations is important.

Successful businesses are "alive" – constantly seeking feedback and evolving in real time to meet the needs of the customer. We have all had negative experiences when seeking a service or a product; many have had negative experiences in their healthcare interactions. Have you ever wondered why, when you share the experience with the business, nothing changes? Most often it is because the business no longer sees the patient/customer as the reason for the day. Instead, they see the patient/customer, incorrectly, as an inconvenience in the day. This cannot be how we approach something as important as new medicine development and the delivery of healthcare. This needs to be addressed now and in a serious way. Patient Centricity, in my view, is the best path to follow.

As I've written earlier, if you are leading change you need to also recognize that many of the senior leaders have decreasing risk tolerances the closer they get to their "best and final" roles and levels. They arrived in their current role through careful navigation and risk management. Why would they jump into a pool of risk at this point in their careers? I realize this statement will be met with vigorous disagreement. We all want to believe we are open to new ideas, the leaders of the future. But the reality is, it is difficult to accept real risk in many circumstances.

In truth, the two best friends of innovation are opportunity and risk. However, when viewed by many leaders, risk is a monster front and center while opportunity is barely visible. It is far off water in the desert. Seasoned and successful executives realize the monster will need to be defended against if confronted, the confrontation will be unpleasant and likely visible to the entire organization. The oasis in the desert will be less noticeable to others in the organization, perhaps unexpected, maybe even a mirage. It will take quite a bit of effort to get there – if you get there at all.

Additionally, most companies, and therefore leadership, look to the past for future guidance. This is a safe approach and mitigates personal risk somewhat because all decisions are based on facts. However, innovation requires a look to the future. While looking to the past can be more familiar and comfortable it often squashes innovation. When things are going well, why change? Additionally, reflection as a mechanism for change is often too slow in responding when things have not gone well. This can place any leadership position that exists within an industry in peril. Looking to the future offers an opportunity to be a market leader but is fraught with challenges.

The future is a muddy landscape that requires persistence from leaders who believe in what they are creating to overcome predictable resistance.

Often, external pressure on the way things are right now is the common denominator of evolution and extinction. How we respond to this external influence decides the outcome. For companies to evolve, we need to apply this pressure to make Patient Centricity a reality. Unfortunately, those companies that do not adapt will likely become extinct.

What is your risk tolerance? What are you willing to sacrifice to make it happen?

While it may appear murky to some right now, I see it as clear as crystal. Patient Centricity will be the next disruptor in pharma. It will provide companies who invest in the systematic integration of the patient perspective into decision-making with a distinct advantage over those that do not. Better resource allocation, a robust pipeline that is aligned with need and value and a workforce that is highly motivated, high performing and highly retained because they are part of something big. Something they were looking for in their careers. They are part of a patient-centered culture.

CHAPTER 7

The Art of Culture

Sustainability Requires A Unified Culture

It was early evening, around 6:30 PM. I had a very long day in the office, starting at 7:30 AM and just finished seeing my 32nd patient at 6:00 when I received the call that there was a patient that required admission to the hospital. I was on call for our four-person internal medicine practice and due to the practice size, being on call would certainly mean a busy night. Feeling a little sorry for myself, I drove to the hospital. It was autumn in Pennsylvania, so it was predictably dark and cool which matched my deteriorating mood.

I had already given the order for the patient to be moved from the emergency room to a bed on a general medical floor – this one on the 9th floor of the hospital. As always, the hospital was bright with lighting and at that hour, with visitors milling about to spend time with their loved ones. The occasional IV pump alarm and somewhat frequent nurse call buzzers could be heard, as well as a few televisions from the patient rooms and some quiet conversations among the nursing staff hustling from patient to patient.

Despite the relative quiet, it was a very busy night and as usual the nurses and aids were working extremely hard. I had talked to and examined the patient I was admitting and was standing at the corner of the nurses' station, writing orders, and completing the admission paperwork. That's when it happened; I experienced the greatest example of healthcare I have ever witnessed.

As I was finishing, I could hear a nurse speaking to a patient in a room near where I was standing. The patient was elderly and clearly in poor health. My impression from what I saw, without any knowledge of the patient or his illness, was that he was near the end of life. The nurse was standing next to the bed on the right side of the patient; her left hand on his right shoulder and her right hand working the dinner tray that sat on his table over his bed. She would scoop some food and talk to him. "Ray, how about a few peas?" she said, slowly moving the food toward his mouth. Between these small bites she said "Ray, today is Thursday and it's a little cold outside. How about some mashed potatoes?". This went on for about 15 minutes, the patient remaining quiet but responding with his eyes and facial expression. This nurse, in each moment, attempted to connect with the patient, to make him feel important, to let him know he mattered to her. This despite a heavy workload and many patients to care for. This was perfection.

I stood there in amazement, realizing that these moments are exactly what care of the person is all about. Delivering a pill or injection, while important, is only part of an advanced care system; a culture developed around the needs of the individual is the foundation of any durable system of care. It's also the foundation of any durable system of medicine development and healthcare delivery.

∞ ∞ ∞

This is core to the idea of Patient Centricity: creating a foundational culture of patient-centered thinking. Without it, the operational components of this function – the active integration of patient insights into all decisions, treatment versus care – would not be sustainable. That nurse feeding the patient that evening, at that moment, was not about nutrition, it was about culture. She believed in her "art." She believed her mission was to connect not only to the patient but the person as well; to help Ray, in this case, in his life's journey at a time when uncertainty was at its highest. She provided care that was more meaningful than simple calories. These magical moments are occurring every day across healthcare systems because of the incredible work of so many people. Why do we pay so little attention to them? Why aren't we modeling systems after this type of behavior?

I believe it is because they are often overshadowed by shortcomings in our systems. This is understandable, to a degree; however, we should be linking these events to necessary changes in the approach we take to encourage more of this. We fail to create environments that can sustain such remarkable interactions. We do not create a living culture on which all activities are based.

The idea of culture runs across industries and is a key part of employee satisfaction, as well as the retention and recruitment of top talent. In an older but still relevant Forbes[6] 2015 survey of more than 1,400 North American CEOs and CFOs over the course of 13 months, overwhelmingly the executives said that healthy corporate culture is essential for a company to thrive. More than 90% said that culture was important at their firms, and 92% said they believed improving their firm's corporate culture would improve the value of the company. Most remarkably, 91% of hiring managers believe a candidate's alignment with culture is equal to or more important than skills and experience.

In that same survey, they believed alignment with culture improved creativity and employee motivation. At the same time, only 15% said their firm's corporate culture was where it needed to be. Does this failure of corporate culture have an impact on employee perception of their work and performance? It certainly does. In 2023, Gallup[7] did a survey of employees in the US finding that only 18% felt actively engaged in their work. Internationally that number was 19%.

While multiple factors contribute to these dismal numbers, one of the noted reasons was lack of connection to the company's purpose. Bells should be ringing, and a common denominator identified. Culture. Some team members will execute according to their cultural expectations despite the organization's efforts in that area. They are the 19%. Others will start with high energy, motivation, and purpose only to see that glow dim as their meaningful effort feels diminished. They feel like goldfish in the ocean. Companies need to do better in creating the environments that their recruitment efforts promise. They cannot expect operational execution to become disconnected from the corporate culture – or lack thereof – that has been purposefully created or ignored. Such expectations are unrealistic and unreasonable. When your workforce appears lethargic and uninterested, look in the mirror, not out the window. Do your part and your teams will do theirs.

Optimizing Operational Activities

To optimize operational activities, the organization requires team members to be aligned on the "why?" Why are we going to work each day? To only develop products that are profitable. No, not in Pharma. To simply deliver medicine? No, not in the delivery ecosystem. High performing workers can support profits and products at any number of companies that manufacture or deliver goods and services outside of healthcare.

Within the healthcare sector, we are privileged to go to work each day to contribute to solution development and delivery for the people who are in need and are waiting. Evident from the many examples of successful businesses, focusing on culture linked to operational activity, aligned with clear objectives, is a necessary and cost-effective way to profitability in any industry. Although we sometimes think we are different, the same is true for Pharma and the greater healthcare space. Focus on need and value, create medicines that are aligned with clinically meaningful results to patients, and deliver them in an environment and in a way that is personal and caring. That is the way to profitability.

When it comes to broadly caring for people, leaders are missing a key component of long-term success if they have not invested in creating and maintaining a unified company culture about, for, and with the patient.

Moving from A Passive to Active Culture

Wishing for a cultural evolution in any company is not a plan. Too often we seek external experts to create a beautiful narrative of how we want the culture to be perceived. This is marketing at its worst and is sure to falter. At a minimum, if this approach is employed, the organization's leaders need to be involved, have a high amount of clarity, and a laser focus on a common point of inspiration. Too often they outsource it all, which places the entire project at risk – even in the face of brilliant support.

Successful culture evolution requires a movement from a passive to an active approach. That means moving from a narrative alone to a narrative aligned with program development that allows each team member in every role and every geography the ability to participate in activities that reaffirms their important contribution in delivering for patients or customers.

How do you develop an "active" culture? By creating programmatic opportunities for every team member, regardless of role, to take part. Team members are hungry for these opportunities. When I have created such programs, I have never seen them have difficulty recruiting interested participants. Remember, in Pharma and the healthcare sector we are already starting with a base that believes in something more than just a job. We onboard people who want to help patients; highly trained and motivated. Many have it all – Head, Heart, and Hands at the start. We lose their Heart when we do not provide them the environment and culture they expected and deserve.

What Works?

Several programmatic approaches have been operationalized and have yielded positive results. These are discussed in more detail in appendix B. For certain, as you institute any programs, you need to understand the baseline engagement within your workforce. Creating honest and unbiased survey questions that allow leadership to truly understand where the employee perspective currently rests.

The roll-out of any program needs to be well defined and well-constructed, understanding the organizational goals and what a unified culture – for the long term – looks like in the best light. Once aligned, it needs to be poured in cement, not laid on sand. It must be the foundation on which everything is built – including HR processes. Metrics need to be developed to identify strengths of the programs and their impact with a continuous process of survey, listen, and adjust, to be certain the programs meet the needs of the team members and serve the company goals. This is especially true of global companies where cultural differences may require slightly different approaches across geographies. Clear measurement of outcomes is important; don't avoid them for fear of less than stellar results. If constructed appropriately, measured consistently, and continuously evolved you will show: It's good business.

There are many types of programs that have had an impact; all involve the team members' active participation. Certainly, these programs are supplemented with passive reminders and narrative. But the key is participation, not reading and listening alone. While we have instituted many different types of activities, I am certain there are many that have yet to be developed. Potential is limited only by our ability to brainstorm and implement. In the future, I can assure you, I will be replicating the programs developed by some readers of this book.

We have focused on education as a cornerstone of our cultural programs, developing an internal University under which all of them sit. The learning programs themselves have four certification levels that allow participants to grow in their knowledge of what a Patient Centric mindset is and ends with them teaching others how they have innovated in this space. They then become part of the University program.

We also have activities that work across geographies. There is Patient Centricity Month where we highlight patients and patient groups as well as the activities of our organization over the previous year. We encourage innovation focused on patient need through Solve-a-Thons, and developed our own approach to a library of inspiration where we would ask employees to use their smartphones to tell their own story. We instruct them on how to record themselves, and asked them five questions, starting with "Why are you working in Pharma?" Perhaps most importantly is the last question: "Tell your family what you do." With enthusiastic participation at all levels of our organization, we are creating a database of hopefully thousands of people who say, "I am here because I choose to help patients, or because I have a family member who has some condition." This has been a significant early engagement step toward an active culture.

My experience with such programs has been quite positive. I have seen hundreds voluntarily enter the first certification level within the University, encouraged and in some cases nominated, by their managers. Solve-a-Thon participation has been from team members across continents and areas of focus. Additionally, with longer-term investments into these projects, it is another example of the company standing behind a patient centric focus. Finally, our month-long focus on the patient has seen more than 30,000 visits to access the content.

One final note on metrics: the impact of these programs on employee engagement in their work has been quite positive: in a pulse survey, more than 80% of team members believe that are contributing to a patient solution. This positivity is in sharp contrast to employee trends in the US and globally.

In Appendix B you will find several programs that serve to engage an active Patient Centric culture. These programs are designed to allow all functions, from researchers to finance team members, to participate and apply the learnings to their work, creating a living cycle of patient centricity learnings linked to patient outcomes.

Culture and the Organizational Attitude

Most remarkably, the daily impact of culture programs becomes readily clear. Teams talk regularly of the "why" – Why are we doing what we do? In my current role, I've heard commercial teams discuss the success of their work in terms of patients served, not simply revenue. We see researchers now discuss clinically meaningful benefits when addressing whether their science should continue to progress in the developmental process.

Senior leaders have also consciously adapted their language to a much more consistent narrative about the patient. One of our commonly used phrases, "patients are waiting" was first stated by the general counsel for the organization. It was during a company Town Hall meeting where she emphasized the importance of the work of the global teams reaffirming the urgency in how we do what we do. She ended her statement with a call to action "patients are waiting."

How remarkable that a chief lawyer in a company, with very little, if any, direct patient contact in her work would think in those terms! It speaks to both the influence of her great leadership and the impact of an active and aligned culture.

Investing in the culture of our companies is not an option. A check-box approach will fall short and uncommitted leaders will use that failure as evidence that culture is not integral to success or that a narrative alone will suffice. I would challenge leaders to make real investments in culture and allow time to develop meaningful measurements as to the impact. It will influence who joins your company, who stays committed to the work, and how well you develop and deliver on the true objectives of the products and services. Patients are waiting.

CHAPTER 8

Improving The Healthcare Ecosystem

Developing Systems That Listen, Act, And Respect The Patient As An Individual

The patient was 92 years old when he passed away in 2021. By all accounts, he lived a great life and did so without many health limitations. With a history of stable coronary disease, chronic renal insufficiency, and four years post-op for an aortic valve replacement he was relatively stable. He was beginning to have some issues walking after six decades of work in construction but still lived with his wife independently at their long-time homestead. He had a clear and sharp mind; he was happy and comfortable.

In September of 2021 he developed cellulitis – a potentially serious bacterial skin infection, where the affected skin is swollen and inflamed and is typically painful – on his left lower leg. Despite outpatient treatment and quite a bit of care at home from his family, it worsened, and he was admitted to the hospital. It was only the fourth time in his 92 years he had been in the hospital, but this time was quite different. COVID cases in the community were quite high requiring him to wear a mask and not leave his hospital room. He was not able to walk freely and sat most of the day. His treatment was somewhat simple – IV antibiotics and local wound care. Along with a hospitalist, he was also being treated by an Infectious Disease specialist.

On day three his blood cultures were noted to be positive; the infection in his leg had gotten into his blood. While he was not having any systemic symptoms such as fever, it could be very problematic for the aortic valve that had been replaced. His antibiotics were changed, and he felt good despite the wound improving very slowly. He, along with the family, asked daily about his discharge; all believing he would be safer at home with less risk of COVID and improved ability to walk around. Everyone, including the patient, was aware he was losing his strength.

Despite multiple discussions with the treating physicians, he remained hospitalized. They didn't seem to have the same perspective regarding his care plan. The hospitalist was more aligned with the family, seeing the benefits of continued antibiotics at home, however, the Infectious Disease specialist refused, preferring to stick to the textbook approach. The family wondered aloud whether the textbook was written with a pandemic in mind. There's an art to caring for people.

The family remained very concerned when another complication arose – a severe nosebleed. An Ear, Nose and Throat

(ENT) doctor was called in, the nose was packed, and the bleeding stopped. Two days later he was ready for discharge, however, the ENT doctor refused to come in on the weekend to remove the packing. Three more days of hospitalization would take place before he was discharged. Three more days of infection risk and minimal ability to ambulate.

By the time he was discharged he was in far worse shape than he was when admitted.

My father, Pasquale, died three weeks later.

∞ ∞ ∞

This is an all-too familiar story, unfortunately. Individualized care of the person has been institutionalized, delivered in medically appropriate but humanely inappropriate ways. To be sure, I do not blame any single person for this outcome. My Dad had multiple problems that certainly would have led to his passing at some point, perhaps in the not-too-distant future. He may have died in the next year, but I don't think it would have been, or should have been, in October. Lost time is tragic and difficult to deal with regardless of how much of it has been accumulated on the ledger.

How do we address a delivery system that is overburdened, that has evolved from personal physicians to institutional care? A system that has lost, in many ways, its connectivity to the patient.

As a start, we need to recognize that patient expectations are not singular or static; they will change over time. Feeling good the service provided today and looking to the past for direction is a formula for failure. We need to be forward looking, alert to shortcomings and quick to fix the problems. We cannot be deaf to the fact that the environment is asking for something, and we're not delivering it and responding, maybe arrogantly at times, with "we know what's best." Think of your interactions with the healthcare system; is there room for improvement?

We cannot reasonably compare the healthcare service sector with others without recognizing the vast differences. The food service industry, for example, has a high bar for customer service and satisfaction. It is quite easy for a customer to find another place to eat if they are unhappy with the quality of food or service. No one's health is at risk, anxieties are usually low; basically, it's not that big of a deal.

Healthcare is quite the opposite. Complexity is high and risk even higher. That is the excuse healthcare systems often cite when they defend their subpar performance in service. I think it makes the opposite argument – it is even more important for healthcare institutions to listen to their customers, adapt quickly and evolve. Changing a provider or system of care is not typically done quickly or without great discernment; healthcare is not an impulse purchase. Changes in hospital processes are necessary immediately for critical issues – certainly, days at the most for less care critical changes – if we are to respect those that put their trust in us. To be clear, while the comparisons are not fully balanced, it places a higher burden on the more critical system that has accepted certain responsibilities when an individual passes through their entrance. Lazy, uninterested fixes are not acceptable.

How many times have you entered a healthcare system and said "Why?"

Why do I feel like I'm not being heard? Anna asked that question about her regularly present and loving family. Imagine the loneliness of a voice in a system that seems to be absent any receptivity. I often saw patients so frustrated during their hospital stay with not being heard they began to feel like hostages. No way to get out and certainly no voice to provide some perspective. My father had that experience despite family members with extensive healthcare experience advocating for him. In such systems, people can feel invisible, seeming to float through and by their care providers but with very little "touch" occurring – the critical human-to-human connection.

Certainly, from the time you enter the admission process you are interacting with humans, but it sometimes feels like an Artificial Intelligence interaction, devoid of empathy and deeper concern. Frequently it is lost on the delivery side that you are interacting with a person at a difficult moment for them. Shoulders are slouched with the weight of worry on the part of the patient and the caregiver. Their minds are not on insurance forms but instead on possibilities of what might be found to explain symptoms, impacts of treatment, or updates from their providers. We cannot expect an equally balanced interaction. Instead, we should enter the engagement with a goal of high efficiency, lowering the stress of waiting endlessly and accepting that your smile may not be met with theirs. Each encounter has components that are common and those that are quite unique. Listening attentively is the only way to discern each, responding like the nurse, with the purpose of the day, the art of our work.

A start, in my view, is to develop a unified culture of patient-centered listening connected to care. More touch points between people; more connecting. This, again, costs systems nothing and will enhance the quality of care, patient satisfaction, and employee engagement. Rewarding care of the person over volume and rigid adherence to methods that are ineffective but accepted. It's good business.

Are these changes impossible? Only if we continue to believe those of us in healthcare are the only providers of knowledge and insight to inform the systems in which we work. Only if we fail to accept what we know to be true – what the rear-view mirror is telling us. It's not working consistently, and we need a reboot.

Let's begin with baby steps, simply listening to those we are caring for – and their families. Individually as workers and together as enterprise systems. Once we listen, we can then begin linking their feedback to actionable change. To be fair to the business, metrics should be developed that are clear and unbiased to measure the outcomes and impacts of these changes. This will not create higher burdens on the system or slower processes. In my father's case, he was hospitalized at least three days longer than necessary; how is that good for any system? It's simply reordering how we deliver care to better align with patient's needs and expectations. This is better for the patient, the families and the employees who will be able to deliver their service in a way that is more rewarding. What could that lead to? I believe that, at a minimum, we would see improvements in retention and burn out rates, with patient satisfaction rates steadily rising.

I spent a good deal of my career in and around hospital systems. The default answer I've heard over the years to the issue of change is "the patient doesn't fully understand." Really? I think it's the opposite, the system doesn't understand.

Say It Again: Patients Have Valuable Insights

The linkage of the need for change in the delivery of care to the drug development space is clear and seamless. Patients do have valuable insights, as do their caregivers.

The Pharma system and the healthcare delivery system are utterly intertwined. Think of it this way: what if, somehow, a hospital system became the utopia of healthcare delivery. They have the best culture, the best doctors, the best nurses, the best length of stay. Every single patient in their system is addressed in the best possible way and they receive zero complaints over a five-year period. But imagine during that time Pharma didn't produce any new medicines? In this scenario, I don't believe we would have moved the needle significantly in a positive direction overall for the patient.

Conversely, Pharmaceutical innovation without healthcare delivery improvement is equally troublesome. If they continue to be separated and left independent of each other the patient is not going to have the level of service or the outcomes they deserve. It is necessary for us to develop the medicines while understanding and addressing, as much as possible, the difficulties that exist in the other parts of the system.

We are flying blind – or hitting blind – if we think we can fix obvious issues in both drug development and healthcare delivery without the meaningful involvement of patients. The system has been persistent in trying it the old way – without patient input or with input and no action. How has that worked out? While there are pockets of improved patient centered activity ongoing, broadly as systems of care, I do not believe we are now more likely to meet expectations than we were in the past. The feedback and data seem to support this. Let us stop repeating the same process: fail, listen, remain unchanged.

We cannot minimize the difficulty of change. Hospitals and care delivery centers can ignore certain problematic components of their systems because they may not directly impact treatment. Waiting times for check in and diagnostic testing, lack of privacy for inpatients, quiet and restful environments, even directed treatment that lacks the touch point discussed earlier. However, there is a business consequence to these failures. Frustration and added stress for patients and families, longer lengths of stay in the hospital, higher staff turnover rates and lower employee satisfaction. Leaders should keep in mind – your competition could be moving faster to resolve these issues than you are.

And while sometimes difficult to measure, those last two employee components can directly impact treatment quality. New hires, erosion of the highest quality staff and poorly satisfied team members translate into lower performance which can, unfortunately, impact quality. Advocates for change need to be certain that their voices are heard while recognizing it is a push and pull solution. Bringing folks to the right level of understanding while helping to find methods to help with change is essential. This will likely not look like a revolution but instead an evolution.

Delivery systems should have a much broader appreciation of patient satisfaction, not just patient outcomes. They should also recognize that satisfaction and outcomes are not completely disconnected. I've had enough experience within hospital systems to know that when pushing departments to improve their game around service, the response that I would typically hear was: "Okay. I hear you. But our priority is keeping people safe. The priority is getting people out healthy."

However, health, safety and service are not mutually exclusive. They are connected under the umbrella of Patient Centricity. My father's example is just one of countless number in which he was in the hospital for an unnecessarily extended period. His circumstances would have undoubtedly allowed for a different set of decisions that would have likely had him discharged in better condition than he was many days later. The system was deaf and unbending. And how did that help the system or the patient? The length of stay was longer, the resource utilization was larger, and the outcome was worse.

Also, a problem can stem from a too-early discharge when the patient lacks the ability to care for themselves adequately in their current state. While on the surface this seems beneficial to costs, how often do these individuals need rehospitalization or more importantly have a more difficult recovery requiring other healthcare expenses over longer periods as outpatients? The simple acts of listening, contemplating and adjusting the approach ever so slightly could result in better outcomes in both instances and would likely cost the system less. It's good business.

It's time we take a serious look at what needs to be fixed and what great looks like. Let's recruit the best in each industry to be certain the right team is on the field and let's maintain the team by providing them with an environment – a culture – they deserve. A culture that encourages them to listen and respond. To contemplate the individual story and to connect, in real ways, that are meaningful to the patient and the team member. We have a clear look at the past that indicates there is room for improvement. Let's not continue to wander down this worn path. Let's now try to look to the future, innovate and evolve and create the road to a patient centric healthcare delivery system.

CHAPTER 9

Building Consensus While Destroying Barriers

Building A Team, Inspiring Leaders, And Creating Metrics

"Follow the path of the unsafe, independent thinker. Expose your ideas to the danger of controversy. Speak your mind and fear less the label of "crackpot" than the stigma of conformity. And on the issues that seem important to you, stand up and be counted at any cost."

– Thomas Watson

I've often used the term "SEAL Team" when trying to convey my vision of how patient centricity should be structured and services delivered. To be clear, my limited knowledge of SEAL Teams is through reading and from what I could gather, they are highly specialized, well prepared, move quickly, are heroes, and would never accept me as one of them. So please understand the reference – it is related to the highly specialized, highly prepared, and fast-moving teams. Patient Centricity teams should remain small and nimble, able to move quickly across functions that need support, and step away allowing them to continue their work.

This is somewhat contrary to traditional Pharma approaches where teams grow over time, become slow and sometimes less relevant while costs to provide support increase steadily. I don't believe support functions that continue to grow in that way, without critical business rationale, are viable in the long-term. The instant a cost-cutting cycle occurs (and it will), these functions are the first to be affected.

Another mantra my teams hear very often from me is that if we are the same one year after another, we are doing something incorrectly and putting at risk the very work we believe is critical. Being good stewards of our work and objectives requires a conscious evolution year after year. We should create new work streams based on organizational and patient feedback; others refined to better align deliverables with expectations. Some discontinued altogether.

Equally Important as what we **do** is making clear what we **don't do** – especially within the patient areas. We do not align our work with any product or brand, and we avoid any inferences that our priority is sales of product over patient benefit. Our teams, for example, will not attend any meetings where the actual sale of a product is the topic. However, we support those functions by sharing our core work: supporting the scientists through research and development, understanding the patient in the real-world setting, and deeply learning and understanding the nuances of behavior. All of this not only helps our ability to create solutions that are meaningful to patients, but also strongly assists the processes of delivery to ensure they are available and accessible.

Why Is Change So Difficult?

I think there is general agreement that change is difficult – especially at an organizational level. Human barriers exist that are predictable, even if the change is difficult to argue against. People fear change and the impact it can have on their work and success. They wonder if they will be held accountable for not instituting a similar change on their own. Others simply oppose anything they did not create – an ego issue.

My career has been equally balanced between creating processes to integrate patient insights into drug development and change management. I've learned a great deal from successes, even more from struggles. However, consistently I've noticed that when change occurs there are five necessary elements:

1. Identify the focus of a unified culture. In healthcare and drug development this should be the patient.
2. Integrate this culture into all HR activities including job postings, interview processes, onboarding, objective setting, and core competencies for each role.
3. Create active educational opportunities and programs to allow active participation for all team members.

4. Institute operational processes that are clear and identifiable to achieve the goals the change is meant to create.
5. Development of qualitative and, when possible, quantitative metrics that can provide the business rationale for continued support as well as the information needed to continually evolve the processes instituted.

Building the Team

What is the best way to proceed with change management? Identifying a need is the first step. Understand the "why" and develop the "how." Discuss it extensively once you have a blueprint and listen to the internal collaborators, acknowledging that not all input will be actionable, but all will be useful in improving the process and understanding the landscape within which change will need to occur.

Once the process is identified, a team needs to be developed. This is a critical step where care must be exercised. The skills needed are important, but the people are the key – identifying those with the skills and experience that are aligned with the "why." It is terrific if the first team members recruited are those whose motivation was present prior to the creation of the process. These folks likely want to apply their skills to the identified objectives and have been looking for a place to focus their efforts. Sound familiar?

Yes – it's about the culture.

One final point about building teams – they need to be appropriately sized. Building empires within companies may be a boost to our egos but it has a short shelf life. Right-sized teams based on portfolio sizes and scope of work is key to durability as a support function. My perspective has been that it is far better to be undersized and arrange support based on organizational priorities rather than be oversized and inefficient. Growth can and will occur as you deliver value and make your argument, through example, and by creating internal champions who benefit from the support they received.

The Leadership Element

Once the Patient Centric process is set up, discipline in leadership will be essential. Continued evolution is integral to this process, and this is best done by listening to your teams. Giving them time to think and create is so important – what I refer to as "white space." I have relied on a white-space concept I refer to as Free-Thinking Fridays where periodically, the global team is asked to block one half day of their schedules and give to their managers a new idea. There are no guardrails around this, they simply must stick to something that will positively impact patients. Many of the evolutionary changes of our Patient Centricity function have been the result of Free-Thinking Friday submissions and subsequent work streams.

Another aspect of disciplined leadership is to continually review what you are not doing and making it clear to your teams what you steer clear of. "Mission Creep" will destroy you. When positive feedback occurs, and you lean into areas that should be avoided, this can lead to a pitfall discussed earlier: growth. Again, don't get caught up in the irrational exuberance of success by continually growing just because you can. While things are viewed positively, you'll have ample opportunity to grow toward your destruction. The system will find you, for certain, and the day of reckoning will come.

While your team leaders will certainly be busy enough to create a need for more help, resist this until the metrics are clear that it is critical to the business. I believe a prioritization approach is best, where all work is not seen as equivalent in value to the organization. If more help is needed, how much of the work done was critical to the business's priorities at the time it was delivered? Often, through prioritization, teams can do less with a bigger impact.

There should be certainty that there are sustainable work requests to support any additional hires. Some questions I contemplate when faced with this: Are we working at 125% capacity? Will the new hire be used while other existing team members are still reasonably busy? To be sure, the discussion cannot simply be about capacity. There needs to be a balance to allow for highly motivated team members to take a breath and think, allow for creativity, and most importantly, time with their families and friends away from work. I can see the eye rolls – great talking points, right? Well, I can say with certainty, through experience, everything written here is achievable, and it will be impactful. We just need to get ourselves and our managers into the habit of not simply asking for project updates but also downtime and white space updates.

We have also created Fellowship and graduate student programs to generate a huge positive impact on keeping the teams fresh and motivated. Having these younger folks join the team provides fresh ideas and new perspectives, both of which are welcome contributions. Often, the Fellows and students see what is being done, provide incredible support and in many instances, offer better ways to deliver our work. The benefit to them has been quite positive as well, providing students with a unique industry experience unavailable elsewhere.

Engaging Corporate Leadership

How do we convert the most senior members of leadership? This is a key question for any program to exist and persist.

First, if a new service of support is being considered, there needs to be at least a minimal level of leadership support. Of course, this could be very superficial and not core to their beliefs. Patient Centricity, for example, is a popular phrase and many leaders feel the need to create something to be sure they are perceived as enlightened. However, support under this structure is still hard fought. In today's environment, if there is a need to argue for the concept of patient insights in new medicine development, I would argue that is not a place where success is likely. However, even with the most minimal support, success can be achieved following the above processes.

Whether there is minimal leadership support or deep support, active and ongoing engagement of senior leaders is important. Their conscious awareness of the work, its impact on internal decision-making, and the impact on patients also translate into a positive corporate reputation. I have found, if leadership is receptive to the concept of patient centricity (customer centricity), the impact on corporate reputation is also important.

I have also relied on Executive Ambassador programs which allow senior leaders to "jump into" a Patient Centricity analysis and deliverables, seeing first-hand how we work with patients, caregivers, and providers, how we deliver these insights within the analysis to internal teams, and how decision-making internally is positively impacted by the collaboration. I have never had an executive or colleague experience the work first-hand and not leave a full supporter.

Metrics Matter

Measurement of impact is a necessary component for long term success. Patient Centricity is a support function, so it is often difficult to identify metrics that can be attributed to this work alone. For example, any one project within Pharma has multiple inputs that are considered in decision-making. Additionally, project timelines are measured in years not weeks or months. Metric creation is a tricky topic; new innovations such as Patient Centricity are repeatedly (and rightfully) expected to show value while more established support functions (HR/Finance) are considered intuitively necessary and are not as frequently burdened with metrics for continued funding.

First, it is necessary to consider both qualitative and quantitative metrics. Some businesses are ultra-focused on quantitative approaches. Pharma, of course, is one of them. We work in a world of biostatistics where p-values drive results. However, as I have argued over the years, a good percentage of decisions in business and in life have a qualitative component. When I leave the house on a cloudy day, do I simply take an umbrella, or do I calculate the odds of needing one? I believe most of us operate daily with information that enhances our many decisions without the influence of mathematics. To be honest, I'm a numbers guy by nature, however, the impact on efficiency and influence on decision-making should not be discounted in business simply because a number is not in the headline.

While quantitative metrics are clearly important, the qualitative impact of support deserves consideration. Have researchers made better and more informed decisions with this patient input? Have programs been altered because of the analysis? Do delivery teams have better insight into the patient in their environment improving their ability to make solutions more available? I think those impacts are very important and need to be part of the evaluation of success. The main point: don't simply dismiss qualitative feedback as less relevant.

Of the quantitative metrics, there are several that are readily apparent. As written, much of the work is measured in years, but we can assess outcomes of analyses linked to final decisions. In the case of Patient Centricity, the work supports medicine development and our teams do not make any final decisions; that is left to the project teams. However, as programs progress internally – as well as competing programs – outcomes can be followed with a comparison of program results and analysis recommendations. We have done this several times and find the results helpful in improving our work and helping internal customers to see down the runway a bit further than perhaps they would otherwise look. An example of this was provided in Chapter 2.

We also follow closely the results of our culture programs. The metrics here are quite a bit easier to produce and follow as most businesses have periodic employee surveys and there are quite a few metrics available within and across industries about employee engagement, recruitment, and retention.

All told, unbiased examination of the work and its impact are necessary to bring the middle majority, as well as senior leaders, into alignment with the Patient Centricity approach.

Regulatory and Government Bodies

The most mature form of Patient Centricity will have internal activities to support the processes needed for Patient Focused Medicine Development and Delivery. However, to raise this to the highest level of impact it requires an outward facing component. Active internal processes should be shared with regulatory bodies and government agencies.

Regarding regulatory bodies, this differentiation of how medicines are developed should affect how regulatory bodies view the context of development. Rightfully, the efficacy, safety, and impact of any new treatment is a priority for review. However, the process of how and why a patient population was chosen, and the input the patients themselves have had in the research and development process should have increasing importance in the review process. This will be especially true when outcomes of the competing development processes are less distinct. Additionally, the patient centricity process for each development plan should be integrated into the regulatory plan such that any meeting with regulatory agencies should include the patient plan from a need, value, clinical impact, and patient point of view.

Government agencies should also have an interest in programs where patient participation is included in new medicine development. If it is ignored by government agencies, they are then batting blindfolded, missing key components of how the end user views the product and how their input was integral to its development.

Building the right-sized team, keeping them focused, maintaining growth discipline, and enlisting the senior most leaders to learn about and support the function is critical. Along with assessment of impact, this is the formula, in my view, to develop your own Patient Centricity "SEAL Team."

CHAPTER 10

A Call to Action

"To be persuasive we must be believable, to be believable we must be credible, to be credible we must be truthful."

– Edward R. Murrow

Dear patients and caregivers waiting impatiently for new treatments,

I appreciate you spending your valuable time with me and my team last week giving us your perspective on the difficult journey you and your family have been on taking care of your child with a rare disease. I want you to know we appreciate you and heard every single word.

We also heard your frustration with the slow progress of science to help treat your baby as well as your anxiety about the future. We sensed your skepticism as to whether we were deeply committed. We heard your anger, if I may say so, about the need to repeat your story. Endlessly you are willing to share these most personal and painful feelings and experiences at the request of folks in pharma and yet you see no progress as a result. Each time, hearing your own words causes pangs of dread within you. You have conflicting feelings about wasting your time, yet maybe, just once, your words will result in action.

How can you not? You see your baby slowly weakening before your eyes. Despite every human effort to the point of exhaustion, nothing you do is slowing the decline. It is clear to us through our discussion that you have created the best environment possible, and your son is comfortable and happy. However, how his story ends will be certain should new treatments not be made available. How can you not share the story again and again, even if you don't believe anything will come of it? You must ask yourself; will my voice ever make a difference?

I'm happy to say this was the time.

Since we spoke, our CEO and leadership have endorsed a full Patient Centricity function. We will be hiring specialized team members to support our researchers, using your words and advice to help direct our program. This will not be a subtle change; it will be an earthquake.

We will also continue to support programs in the development space, and we will be connecting more closely with patients and their families to learn more about their challenges in their real-world setting. This will help us solve one of the problems you mentioned to us – an understanding of patients and their caregivers beyond the disease. We will concentrate on understanding behavior to be more inclusive to a diverse population across the world.

Remarkably, our company has doubled down on our focus on patients. We have invested in programs that will create and maintain a culture that thinks about your little boy every day, in every role. This will ensure what you have helped us achieve will be sustainable.

My promise to you is that we will transition all you have s. us into action. Your time is not wasted. While we can nt understand your experience or that of your son, we will work to best understanding possible.

We are all-in with you, committing to allocate all of our efforts to help your little boy. While there is no certainty in the results of our effort there is complete certainty in the method. We will work every day – with you – to make new solutions available. You, your family, and your son are the "why" we do what we do. We recognize the professional privilege we have working with patients, and we will be relentless in our efforts.

Thank you for your partnership.

Sincerely,

Patient Centricity Officer

Wouldn't you love to write such a letter? To work in a space that delivers what is in there? You can. Now is the time to start constructing your note to your patients – the changes you make will lead to better Research, Development, and Delivery processes. One that is with patients and for patients. One that commits in words, actions, and investments for the patients we aim to serve.

Start writing your letter, taking from my words and experiences in this book any and all that would be helpful. We are not competing in this space. We need to work together to listen, learn and act. We need to do whatever is necessary to bring better solutions to those who are waiting – faster.

These changes will not be easy, but they will be worthwhile. They will not be without risk – professional risk, risk of failure – but nothing worthwhile is risk free. "Persistence in the Face of Resistance" will be written on your shield. But compare any of that to the journey of the patient, their caregivers, their family, and friends. No contest.

Their journey is the reason for our day in Pharma and the healthcare delivery system.

For every patient story there is a team member story as well. Sometimes the story is a combination of both – a team member who is also a patient. I encourage each of you to build patient centricity processes which create opportunities for team members to inspire each other.

So, I ask each reader whether in Pharma, healthcare delivery, a patient, a caregiver, or an interested individual: what is your story? What inspires you when you think of helping those who are in need of a healthcare system? Have you had experiences that you can reflect on? Do you believe strongly in something you experienced and would like to influence? No matter your role or place, you are a valuable contributor to this effort. Your story will inspire and encourage others to share their journey. It is through our joined efforts that meaningful change will occur. Now is the time!

How We Move Forward

While we can't ignore conflict within institutions resistant to change, we can have a respectful approach. No one ever fully joined an effort with their Heart because they were ridiculed or demeaned. Let's make this change together, understanding that some folks, including leaders, may take a bit more time to arrive in a place you see as self-evident. With so much going on in the world and our lives, so many demands, can we have a call to action?

This is for us all: patients, healthcare workers, pharma, insurers, government agencies, and those who will be patients or caregivers. Anyone left? We can make the change.

Every hospital system should consider creating a Patient Centricity Officer role or something similar, whose only job is to ensure the patient still is the focus of work and a culture of patient focused delivery of services is alive, strong, and sustainable.

Larger systems would be best to place this this role in the C-Suite, otherwise it will get reduced to fighting for airtime and the barriers can become insurmountable. What decision in a delivery system should be made without patient involvement?

Within Pharma the Patient Centricity role should exist and be leveled at the C-Suite or close to it. The role should be highly visible and have the authority of leaders of more established functions such as regulatory and medical affairs. It is important that the perception and reality of the patient role be equal to the traditional

C-Suite representation. Patient voice should be present whenever operational, strategic, commercial, and R&D voices are present.

For those who don't agree, rather than argue the positive impact, I would simply challenge them to present the downside to this approach. I don't believe there are any. Would corporate reputation be damaged by patient centricity representation at the leadership level? No. In fact it would likely be enhanced. Would decision-making be negatively impacted? Nope. In fact, it will be enhanced each time the patient's perspective is actively integrated into any decision tree being considered.

Lastly, for those leaders who dismiss this call to action with the all-too-overused response: "we are already doing that," I say: prove it. Patients deserve more than your assurances. Show us how you have affected decisions in research, development, and delivery with robust patient input. Show us how you obtained the patient insights, integrated them into analyses that are specific and actionable along the developmental continuum. Share how you evaluated the patient in the real-world setting to better provide a comprehensive understanding of patient need. Explain how you went to great depths to understand behavior and how it affects the delivery of care. Show us how you specifically invested in culture.

If you refuse, I'm doubtful there is much there beyond the narrative. If you do have a story to tell, then we will all be better for it – help us get to where you are. We cannot link Patient Centricity to the competitive approaches as an industry. It is pre-competitive, and we all need to communicate our best practices, put aside our egos and move down this path toward a Patient Centric Healthcare system together.

Only then will Anna, Stephen, Tommy and Tim, Linda, the Nurse and Ray, Carol, Pasquale, and countless others be given the respect they deserve for sharing their most personal story and teaching us all the true lesson of being Patient Centric.

CONCLUSION

We have covered a lot of ground here – some areas discussed in more detail than others – but the focus has never changed. It is about all of us; current and future patients and caregivers. A very big bucket: big enough to hold each one of us because, unfortunately, we all have a reservation with the healthcare system, we simply don't know the specific time.

The healthcare ecosystem, broadly defined, includes (but is certainly not limited to) those companies that develop solutions and those that deliver them. In this book, I've tried to make evident the connectivity of those two systems – Pharma and healthcare delivery. I believe this connection is not readily apparent to many, and if not recognized, the opportunity to significantly impact the system of care for the individual will be lost, and we will continue to have more challenges year over year. Beyond the learnings, I've also tried to make clear the part each of us can play in this evolution.

I've shared some of what has inspired me in my life and my work. What inspires you can be very different. All the better; share your story and we can inspire each other.

For those leaders in Pharma, Biotech and Healthcar Patient Focused Medicine Development and Deliver happening. The only question is whether it happens to you o you. Start thinking about the role of the patient, actionable methods to listen and act, regular measurement of successes and challenges, and sustainability of what you've created. This evolution requires not just words and good intentions, but real work and real change.

Have a look at the culture of your organizations and pay close attention to those that execute at the highest level. Coordinate and act by creating a programmatic approach to culture change. Assess the results and continue to change for the better.

Importantly, do not become obsessed with quantitative metrics alone. It is the primary battle flag of some I've run into over the years – and has been a frequently asked question of those in the 2.5% of late adopters. It is likely the most frequently asked question of those who have read this book and who don't buy into my approach. It is a fair question but I ask for your indulgence and contemplation with what I've written on this. It should be recognized that the decisions made within Pharma or within a hospital system are comprised of multiple inputs, each weighted differently. The Patient Centricity function is not decisional; instead, it is a critical ingredient among many inputs. As such, it is difficult and likely not completely rational to decide the weight of the inputs into project team decision-making or to isolate one of many. Without patient input, I have said, we are hitting blindfolded, missing critical inputs necessary for success.

Over the years, I have avoided the bait of creating quantitative metrics to satisfy that question when in reality the metrics do not offer measurement of impact. An example: one could easily track the number of patient engagements, number of completed assessments, number of teams supported, disease areas addressed, publications on patient related topics. Each may offer some idea of how busy the teams are, but none offer a glimpse into how the work has impacted decision-making. Forty assessments completed, none of which assisted research teams in understanding the patient or in decision-making would be a wasted effort. I'd much prefer to understand our internal customer needs, how they approach transition points and whether our support has influenced, in a positive way, their programs. Too many times we are challenged, unreasonably, by standardized approaches that simply don't apply to the work being executed. Allowing the demand for quantitative metrics alone to be the expectation of success places the team and the work in a deep pit from which it is difficult to escape once entered.

I have, however, discussed some of the quantitative methods I've employed to assess the longer-term program outcomes that included our recommendations; patience is required here.

One additional barrier I have experienced over the years, which I am sure is familiar to many of you as well: complexity. The issues discussed, I've been told, are so complex it is naïve to think that patient involvement can solve the development and delivery dilemma. I have two responses. First: not being able to fix everything is no argument against trying to fix something. I've been clear in this book that while Patient Centricity is a big step forward, it is not the only change that needs to accompany a full healthcare system reboot.

And my second response: you will be surprised by how far you can go by listening to the people you're trying to serve.

Consider the electric vehicle industry. The complexity of mining raw materials, building batteries, improving the durability of a charge, reconfiguring production lines to build the vehicles, creating a charging infrastructure, and educating consumers were and remain challenges. Each of those issues required solution development across sub-industries (as well as public-private collaborations) and none were solved simultaneously. However, each improvement moved the industry closer to where it needed to be. The first cars produced had very little range and less-than-ideal quality, while public charging stations remained few and far between. But customers were part of the solution process. While they may not have understood the physics of energy storage and consumption, they understood what they wanted: a car that could go longer distances between charges and ubiquitous charging stations that would relieve "range anxiety." While the EV industry continues to face headwinds, there is no denying their progress toward a consumer aligned product.

Improving the processes for those in the healthcare system requires similar determination and involvement from the patient. So, if you confront this complexity, don't let it tie you up in knots.

Push forward anyway. Show value in the work and let the improvements – over time – speak for your efforts.

Cultural programs can and should be assessed in real-time. Most, if not all, companies have regular surveys of their teams and from those surveys you can glean positivity rates, motivation, corporate culture perception, as well as recruitment and retention impacts. From my experience in this area, the results of active engagement of team members in programs designed to support the culture have been quite positive. We have seen 82% of our team members believe their work is an important driver of value creation and delivery; 80% have a clear view of how their work connects to the company's purpose of bringing value to patients, and 70% believe the company makes a significant effort to secure the patient perspective. Compare these results to the employee positivity rates shared earlier in the book, topping out at 18-19%. Culture matters and it is good business.

The strategic and tactical examples I've shared do not represent perfection but instead progress. Replicate them, or even better, adjust them in some form to address the needs of your own organization, assess the results, and share them so we all can benefit.

What has been the impact of this work?

The work of Patient Centricity continues to support hundreds of activities globally every year across the medicine research, development, and delivery continuum. Importantly, the five teams within Patient Centricity, each with their specialized approach, create a workflow that provides support from the time a molecule moves from the mind of a scientist and into the research lab, thorough clinical development and into the marketplace. Each step has a place where the patient voice is heard and is present in decision-making.

Also, when companies proceed with change, often referred to as transformation, the cultural foundation is more important than ever. This is not the time to walk away from it, but instead re-emphasize a strong culture.

We've seen researchers not only integrate the early assessments in their work but also consider it a standard "business as usual" component of research projects. They now ask the question of clinically meaningful benefit and have altered their direction based on the analyses of patient need and perceived value. Additionally, the early Patient Centricity support team (Medical Intelligence and Patient Insights – MIPI) is regularly called upon for assistance on indication selection and outcomes of value to patients.

This work has been so tightly integrated into the discovery and research function that one unit leader has turned the team acronym into a verb, asking his team "has the project been MIPI'd." This collaboration has increased the likelihood that outstanding science is linked tightly with value and need, that the best indication is chosen, and those projects that enter clinical development are aligned with outcomes which patients are seeking. Said another way, patients will seek out these solutions because they matter to them.

As stated above we are following closely all recommendations provided to research teams and determining the accuracy of the assessments over time. This is a longer-term metric as project success or failure is most often measured in years. We do, however, follow the rationale for changes in programs as they occur that would point toward a Patient Centricity influence, such as indication selection and patient population benefit. These pieces of information can provide a quantitative peek – a snapshot – into the impact of our work. As I've written, since this work began several years ago, we have seen indication selection modified, programs terminated, and refinements made based in whole or in part on the input of the Patient Centricity team.

However, as the work progresses, more will follow on this.

The qualitative impact of the work is clear; project teams overwhelmingly believe the analyses provide enhanced decision-making and has positive impacts on outcomes of their programs. Importantly, they also feel more connected to the patients they are working to serve. For those building Patient Centricity programs, this is one of the strongest sustainability factors: internal teams demanding the service. Leadership hears this loud and clear.

The Patient Insights and Solution team (PInS) has evolved over the years to concentrate not only on the patient in the real world setting but also in bringing the patient experience inside the organization to internal teams. They have done so using technology (eg: Virtual Reality) and this has had very strong influence on internal team member's understanding of the daily experience of the patient. The PInS team works closely with development, medical, and commercial, filling the gaps in knowledge of the patient experience beyond the illness. Most of the impact data for this team is in the qualitative category – how has the programmatic approach to this additional patient information prepared the teams and the organization to better deliver solutions. While quantitative real-time measurement is difficult, reflection and review of past failures can be quite clear. We regularly contrast previous unsupported program outcomes and the gaps identified with current support processes. Again, the feedback is overwhelmingly positive.

The Behavioral Science Consortium (BSC) works across the entire organization but primarily supports the development, medical, and commercial teams. As with all Patient Centricity functions, every work stream is brand agnostic with the focus on the patient: their journey, needs, and barriers they face to achieving the best care possible. This team creates deliverables based on questions internal teams may have and produces the analysis in a curricula format; that is the learnings can and are applicable to the current work stream and can also be applied across projects and to a general learning format. This team also makes available their work for publication. The Behavioral team's feedback from internal customers has been extremely positive. Again, the sustainability of much of this work can be supported by this internal feedback as well as the current extended queue for support. Ultimately, these learnings can be utilized by patients and patient groups as well as providers and health systems to improve how they interact with each other as well as the pharma component of care.

None of the above would be possible without a strong team with energetic, persistent and focused execution. As I referenced in an earlier chapter, the right people aligned with culture make it all possible. I am fortunate to have such a team - leaders, managers and team members - I am thankful for each of them and their efforts. They looked at a blueprint and showed the structure could be built. But the structure could only be built on fertile ground and that is the organization: researchers, development teams, commercial, legal, HR, Finance, Ethics and Compliance, Procurement and so many more. Through their belief in the mission and willingness to give it a go we have started something remarkable together.

For those who continue to believe that a Patient Centricity function isn't necessary or that the work of your organization is already patient centric: Again, I ask, please share your results. Additionally, if you want the work to evolve and improve over time a formal Patient Centricity function is something that should be considered. Do you have an ethics and compliance function? Legal? I assume your expectation is for everyone in the organization to behave ethically and in legally compliant ways. Wouldn't the same apply to Patient Centricity? The goal should surely be a patient centric organization; after all, it is the ultimate measure of success. However, who will be tasked with reflecting, evolving, assessing and ensuring the sustainability of the function?

As with the Legal, Ethics and Compliance example, there needs to be an expertise in-house that can be relied upon for direction. Patient Centricity, structured appropriately, provides that expertise and, I hope I have shown, is a highly specialized function. And it's good business.

Finally, some words of encouragement from the 18th century. Benjamin Franklin shared this fable about a father and son traveling with a donkey. When the father rode and made his son walk, they were criticized by those they met; likewise, they were criticized when the son rode and made the father walk, or when they both rode the donkey, or when neither did. So finally, they decided to throw the donkey off a bridge. The moral, Franklin wrote, was that it is foolish to try to avoid all criticism.[8]

There is no doubt that the path forward will not be without its challenges. Change is always difficult. There will be criticism regardless of the pure intention of what you are trying to achieve. Expect it. But never lose focus on the importance of this mission and the many people – each one of us – that will benefit from your work. The journey has begun and the destination certain. Now, with energy, positivity and willingness to fight, let's go!

"If you have an apple and I have an apple and we exchange these apples then you and I will still each have one apple. But if you have an idea and I have an idea and we exchange these ideas, then each of us will have two ideas."

G.B. Shaw

END NOTES

[1] https://www.lek.com/insights/ei/biopharma-launch-trends-lessons-learned-leks-launch-monitor

[2] https://www.lek.com/insights/ei/biopharma-launch-trends-lessons-learned-leks-launch-monitor

[3] Business Wire - February 28, 2023: WE Brands in Motion Health Study: Corporate Reputation Is Leading Factor in Prescribing Decisions

[4] Gallup SEPTEMBER 13, 2023, Retail, Pharmaceutical Industries Slip in Public Esteem

[5] Pharmaceutical Research and Manufacturers of America, PhRMA Annual Membership Survey, 2022

[6] https://www.forbes.com/sites/susanadams/2015/11/12/corporate-culture-matters-says-new-study/?sh=5c5a194822b4

[7] Gallup WORKPLACE JANUARY 25, 2023 U.S. Employee Engagement Needs a Rebound in 2023

[8] Benjamin Franklin: An American Life. Walter Isaacson. 2003

APPENDIX A: OPERATIONAL TRANSFORMATION

The operational approach to Patient Centricity is the engine. This is the way to patient-focused medicine development and delivery and requires discipline in execution to be certain it is not diluted in content to preserve the existence of the name and intention.

This is real; it's brick and mortar, not smoke and mirrors. It requires an investment and a very intentional approach to build the proper teams that can execute in material ways to affect decision-making. These teams should be highly specialized, and the tactical approach should parallel the entire research, development, and delivery process. The teams need to be configured in such a way that their specialization aligns with the needs of their internal partners.

First, my definition: the actionable integration of patient insights and perspectives in all decisions that impact the development of patient treatments and solutions.

Patient Centricity Organizational Structure

TEAM 1
Discovery and Research
Partnering with internal Teams to analyze and integrate the patient perspective from discovery through early development

TEAM 2
Development and Real-World Experiences
Providing actionable insights based on a holistic understanding of the patient in the real-world setting: utilizing data, technology and qualitative research methods

TEAM 3
Understanding of Behavioral Science
Enhancing organizational understanding of patient behaviors in their environments

TEAM 4
Partnering Globally with Patients
Building trusted relationships globally with patients and advocacy organizations

TEAM 5
Culture and Integration
Creating a global culture focused on the patient for every employee in every role

To achieve this, four teams were created, each with a specific remit and points in the developmental continuum where their work could align with the traditional drug development and delivery process. This is a key component of change management: the new processes are built to enhance the way research and development works. It is intended to be an evolution not a revolution. This encouraged leaders in those areas to listen and avoided the tendency for a defensive posture. This is where it started, however, the impact was verging on revolution.

For example, the team structured to support discovery and research was built on the idea of bringing the exam room into the research labs. How best could we link the patient perspective as well as the delivery of new solutions in the real world to a deeper understanding by researchers of the potential and challenges around the science they were working on? This was achieved by utilizing the patient perspective, that of the HCP and caregiver blended into an analysis that also considered the standard of care, competitive landscape, the patient journey, entry points into the treatment continuum, and the science, as well as other components.

It was through this highly specialized analysis from this team that real discussions began to take place as to whether the molecule could achieve what was expected from patients and their healthcare providers. The idea of clinically meaningful benefit – as described by patients – began to be a regular talking point in research meetings. This has led to these analyses contributing to disease area focus as well as portfolio prioritization.

A second team focused on the patient in the real-world setting. How do we translate our learnings from clinical trials and adapt to delivering these solutions to the much more complex and diverse environments in which patients live? This team looks at multiple components of the patient in their environment to help development and delivery teams understand barriers to good care and the complexities patients face each day. This team also evaluates the patient as an entire individual. What are the symptoms beyond the condition we are trying to treat that are impacting their feeling of well-being? Fatigue, anxiety, depression, insomnia could be a few of these challenges. If we are going to go beyond treating the patient to caring for the individual, these points of concern are critical for us to be aware of to achieve that goal. Understanding the delivery system is also a key part of the work of this team. What good is any solution if a patient does not have access to it? If they can't receive necessary follow-up appointments or diagnostics? This is the link between the pharma world and the delivery system I raised earlier in the book.

Behavior is a critical part of patient care – some studies say 50%, while others say as much as 70% of outcomes can be attributed to behavior. The point is not the number but the recognition that not addressing the behavioral component is a missed opportunity. The 4th team deployed in a mature patient centricity function is a behavioral team. Understanding the behavioral drivers of care and actions that promote or obstruct adequate care is essential to deliver solutions.

There are many instances when the patient may not raise a concern to their provider due to embarrassment, anxiety, or even the dismissal of the concern as "it's just a part of life." What if the provider doesn't ask about it? This is the conundrum many patients find themselves in. This is even more frustrating when treatments are available to address the issue. The behavioral t
to better understand the reasons behind this and d
for delivery teams to resolve it. This can be done t
constructed educational condition-specific litera

seminars to help interactions become more natural. There are many other methods of deployment of this team to learn and educate the patient, caregiver, provider, and internal teams.

One point on this team and the entire patient centricity function within pharma that I will reiterate: they should be product agnostic. The work should help all patients in all environments to receive any treatment that is best for them as decided upon by discussions with their providers. Internal teams learn through this work on how best to deliver their solutions. However, the education and the delivery are distinct and separate. To that end, the behavioral teams should develop a clear charter that delineates the scope of their work; what they will do and most importantly what they will not do. This charter should be made available to all departments in the organization and all leaders should recognize and accept the guidelines of the charter as the standard operating procedure for the patient centricity behavioral team.

The final team is dedicated to developing long term relationships with patients and patient groups. These relationships should be constructed so they are bi-directionally beneficial, are non-transactional, and diverse in geography and composition of patients. This team should execute globally and take the time to develop relationships through a mutually beneficial model in which they share their perspectives, and we share our expertise in the way of educational opportunities, access, and transparency.

We need to remember – and not take lightly – the fact that when ...tients speak to us, they are sharing the most personal and often troubling details of their life. This information needs to b at all costs and respected without exception. My promi groups when I started in this space was that when they share their stories, I guarantee the information will be protected and will be used in a decisional way. They are not wasting their time when working with my teams. If you are working in this space or building capabilities this cannot be overemphasized: don't ask for this information unless you are ready to utilize it in a material way. These folks are continually asked to share their story and often they receive no follow-up or feedback. Think about the message that sends to the individual: their information is not appreciated and respected.

Importantly, the engagement team needs close partnerships with legal and ethics teams as they develop processes for execution of their work. These teams are educated about the rules and regulations of engagement in the geographies across the world, and they are the evangelists for protecting and respecting the patient voice in all interactions. As with the behavioral teams, this team should develop a charter and standard operating procedure to allow for a legal, compliant, and ethical business-as-usual approach to their work.

Aside from the highly specialized work and interactions of the above teams I delineated them in detail for another reason. In pharma we use language quite loosely. If you were to ask someone what patient engagement is, you would likely get several answers – some narrow, many too broad. We need to demand clarity from companies as to the work they are doing; it is only then that we get beyond talking points and into the work of patient-focused medicine development and delivery.

Engaging patients is a critical part of Patient Centricity but, in isolation, it is not the encompassing work of a mature function. Engagement needs to be linked to specialized teams that have partner functions with the research, development, and delivery continuum. To be impactful, these teams need to create analyses that integrate components that are traditional (science in research) with critical components that have been absent (patient, caregiver, HCP insights, need, value) to change the way decisions are made. That is the most critical point: these analyses should affect decision-making. Then and only then will the patient voice be heard in every research lab, development team meeting, and delivery systems in the places where they live.

APPENDIX B: CULTURAL TRANSFORMATION

The cultural component of patient centricity is foundational. All other tactical approaches necessary for integration of the patient perspective in new solution development will fail – or at the very least will not be sustainable – without organizational culture evolution.

While culture may be the foundation of sustainability, education is the cornerstone of culture.

The Power of Education

In Pharma and the healthcare delivery system, the focus of a unified culture should be on the patient. This needs to go beyond the narrative and encompass all aspects of services. To achieve this, process creation needs to integrate all team members actively into cultural activities.

I believe the most efficient method of creating cultural programs is through an educational platform. Creation of a university, of sorts, which allows a growing number of programs to exist along with formal curricula to ensure the organization has the basic access to the knowledge necessary to promote a unified culture while delivering on the associated mission of the firm. In the case of pharma, my concept of this was the Patient Centricity University (PCU). The PCU is a curricula-based learning platform with four certification levels. Each of these levels encompassed a growing knowledge of a patient-centered mindset and actions, starting with the basics of engaging patients and expanding to the best methods of integrating patient insights into the work of the participant, regardless of discipline, as their learning progressed. The highest certification level involves the participant sharing an example of how they successfully integrated patient centricity into their work – the process, the objective, and the results. This would be presented to senior leaders and ultimately, that example and the individual would be integrated into the future learning modules within PCU. The student becomes the teacher.

The power of this process has been remarkable. Team members from across the globe have signed on for entry into the first level certification programming.

This concept, the creation of internal learning platforms to enhance culture and performance, is transferrable to any industry. While the curriculum would need to be adjusted to align with the core goals of the company, its customer base and their expectations, the process and metrics would be consistent.

This is not a small or easy task; the difficulty lies not in the concept but in the execution. Very few companies will resist the idea of cultural enhancement. However, few may see it as a prioritized critical business need. It requires long-term thinking and commitment to the concept to understand that the financials will be positively impacted by its success. This impact begins with recruitment of talent, continues with retaining talent, and is emphasized by the energy and creativity of the workforce. Why is it so difficult to execute? Distractions and the lack of persistent energy behind the idea. Who is going to champion this as their job? Who would balance the more traditional metrics (eg: profit) with the less traditional around culture (eg: employee positivity)? In healthcare, it is the work of Patient Centricity.

To be clear there is a great deal of work to be done. I have written about the poor employee positivity in the US and Globally in chapter 7. One can debate these statistics, however, let's look back on performance and results. It's pure nonsense to think we have no room for improvement. Let's talk about what works in culture development.

First, my definition: the conscious awareness of the patient for every employee, in every role, and in every geography, every day.

The work of the patient centricity team in culture is to deeply understand the organization composition: who are the team members, where are they located, and how close are they to patients in their work. Programs will then need to be developed to take the narrative of culture and, as I've written repeatedly, make it actionable. Programs that all employees can take part in, can learn which they can integrate the learnings into their work. not simply a generically more motivated work force. It rce that believes deeply in what they are doing, feels their participation every day is contributing to the care of patients and their health and actively contributes each day in the work of the company. The Head, Heart, and Hands.

Convincing people this is the best path is the lowest bar (Head). Having them believe they are contributing is a bit more difficult but can be achieved through meaningful program development, participation, operational success, as well as the success of the overall organization (Heart). The actionable integration of the culture into their work is quite advanced and requires ongoing education and exposure to methods to do so (Hands).

A passive to active programmatic approach to culture development will deliver significant results. You will not only see a motivated workforce, but one that is aligned and much more collaborative naturally. Higher retention rates and more successful recruitment should also be a measurable result. Most importantly, team members feel more positive about their work and their contributions.

Companies should accept that an investment in culture needs to be made and move beyond a company-created narrative alone avoided. A vicious cycle of lack of culture, poorly motivated team members, lack of creativity, poor recruitment and retention, and poor collaboration will lead to significant disadvantages over the medium- and long-term within any industry. Perhaps now I've touched on metrics that even skeptics can digest?

Tactics

Some of the cultural programs that have been impactful and can be applied across sectors:

1) Patient Centricity Month: a dedicated month where a reflection on the successes from the previous 12 months, ideas and objectives for the next 12 months. Available globally is in-depth programming based on an annual theme. The insights from senior leaders, patients, and patient groups from around the world are all contained within the agenda. Patients and patient groups are involved, and a global perspective is targeted. The content is currently translated into 9 languages and live activities are available for the different time zones across the globe. Many senior leaders actively participate. Global team members are highly engaged with over 30,000 "hits" to the site where content sits. This is the "training camp" of Patient Centricity. While our obvious goal is patient centric behavior and focus every day of the year, Patient Centricity Month is an intensive retreat of sorts – designed to celebrate successes, focus on the next phase of strategy, and reinvigorate the motivation and creativity of our entire organization for the year ahead.

2) Solve-a-Thon: an open and global request for proposals on how to better impact patient outcomes. Employees from all functions are asked to form teams as they see fit and develop ideas that would address an identified gap in care and a solution that could positively impact patient outcomes. They put together a preliminary business plan and pitch their idea. Second round finalists are assigned mentors from senior leadership, placed in a business accelerator, and prepare for a pitch session that includes live and video components as they ready for judging. Winners are chosen in a weighted fashion by both senior leaders and votes submitted by team members from across the organization. Winners are funded and senior leader mentorship provided for the next year. This program has garnered significant interest worldwide and multiple countries have taken part.
3) Stars In the Sky: video testimonial voluntarily submitted by team members globally. They are given 5 prompts (questions) to answer on a self-shot video. The idea here is to create a large catalogue of motivation to inspire each other while also allowing team members to create a private library of their videos for their personal reflection. This approach creates positive momentum and advances the concept that all Patient Centricity functions should be aspiring to; it is not about the Patient Centricity team alone being patient centric but every team member across the

organization.

4) Patient Centricity University (PCU): All the above is included under the umbrella of PCU. Additionally, PCU has a full curriculum that helps team members understand the idea of what patient focus means to them, how to learn methods of understanding the patient and the importance of behavior and how to integrate these learnings into their work. The highest certification level, Innovator, requires the student to present a case example of how they applied their learnings into their work that resulted in a positive patient impact. Senior leaders should be expected to hear this presentation and the student, post example, will then integrate their example into the PCU curriculum. The student becomes the teacher.

All these programs need to be fully and seamlessly integrated into the operations of the company and recognized by leadership. Team members should be able to identify the opportunities provided as part of the fiber of the organization and as a "higher calling." This can only be achieved if the belief in these systems is visibly endorsed at the top. If this is seen as temporary or expendable – nice to have but not essential – it will never reach the potential it has to impact the organization.

One approach for making these programs "sticky"? Metrics. This is where quantitative metrics are important. Be certain that whatever programs are developed, clear goals are shown at the start, and they are socialized. I have addressed this previously -

through both qualitative and quantitative measurements.

A steady trend upward in employee satisfaction and their belief they make a meaningful contribution to the success of the organization should be seen in pulse surveys. There should be clear improvements in recruitment and retention of top talent as well.

In my experience I have seen employee satisfaction be positive for eight of ten employees. Their feeling of effective collaboration is seven in ten. These numbers are dramatically better than the baseline within the same pool of employees and far better than averages across industries.

Importantly, culture transformation changes the dialogue. As an example, over the years, during leadership meetings, the discussion consistently revolves around "how can we have an impact on the patients" or "what are the best ways to deliver these solutions to the patients that are waiting for them?" This is remarkable when the business first approaches the need of the patient as a path to product success!

ACKNOWLEDGMENTS

First, of course, my wife, Karen, and our four children Patrick, Gina, Nicholas and Elisa. Constant sources of inspiration, energy, and support.

Karen's patience and counsel, dosed regularly and lovingly throughout my journey, made this all possible. When my frustrations in creating this process peaked, her calm reminder of the "why" would put me back on track. Her persistent nudging for over a decade to write this book is the reason I kept at it.

I am so grateful to my family, where my story began and continues. My parents, Palma and Pasquale, who provided a life foundation built on cement. My sisters, Annmarie, Maria, and Lisa who have always provided solid and consistent support for their younger sibling. Maria kept us alive and entertained during the lean years of medical school…so appreciated!

This all began long ago with an idea and no guarantee of success. My early teams, with whom I started this journey, trusted in me and this concept because of their commitment to patients – even when it presented more risk than reward to their careers. I am forever thankful and hope you always remember the important work you started.

Other colleagues supported my efforts selflessly, for the good of the work and the patients who would benefit. While there were many who contributed I want to recognize some of those individuals specifically.

Alexandra Kropotova is a friend and colleague for whom I will be forever thankful. She was the first person who heard this idea. She easily could have ignored my pitch but instead she chose to listen and believe. She is simply a great leader. Her support and her network literally got this from an idea to a pilot process.

Julie Clauss was one of the earliest supporters of this work. Had she not utilized her network to expand mine, it is likely this effort would not have gotten much beyond the pilot phase. She risked a great deal professionally in supporting a very early patient focused process by creating opportunities for me to be heard. I am forever grateful.

Andy Plump, an experienced Pharma Executive and scientists, championed a patient-focused approach by listening to an idea before it could be shown effective. His early endorsement and ongoing support, including access to his network, accelerated patient involvement in new drug development.

Elias Zerhouni, physician, pharma executive and former Head of the NIH, is a remarkable leader. His forward leaning style and curiosity for innovation allowed me the opportunity to pitch an idea that was new in Pharma. His support systematized the early version of my work across a large global company. I was fortunate to have his patient-focused leadership and influence endorse this idea from the beginning and am forever thankful.

Aurelie Grienenberger created many opportunities for my ideas to be heard by organizational leaders in the very early days of this work. I am thankful for her commitment to patients and faith in the process.

I am indebted to my current leadership team – Doug Noland, Lisa Mattle, and Chad Stewart – for their relentless work on behalf of patients and their innovative spirit in bringing to life the ideas mentioned in this book. I am always amazed at their energy and resilience, focus and commitment. The work of future patient centricity teams will owe a debt of gratitude to each of them for paving the way despite many obstacles.

To all those who work within Patient Centricity – past and current – know the impact you all are having and will continue to have every day with every activity. Success would never be possible without your efforts and I am sincerely thankful for all you do.

I would also like to recognize Tyler Marciniak. While Tyler worked with us, his contribution to the integration of the work into active processes was incredible. His organizational skills and process management approach helped accelerate the visibility of this work globally.

For most of the implementation of this work, Joe Collins has had a critical role. Joe was an early and current member of my Leadership Team and has been a partner on this journey for more than a decade. He joined the patient centricity movement when it was barely moving, leaving behind an established and successful run on the commercial side of the business to do so. When I pitched the idea of him joining the two-person team (including me) it was with more hope than optimism. His leap of faith reveals his commitment to patients and his contribution to the work has been incalculable. How things evolved – especially in those early days – was strongly influenced by his efforts.

To the research teams who have openly accepted this "new" idea of patient inputs into your work as well as the Medical, Development and Commercial teams we have supported – you are true innovators whose head, heart, and hands will impact far more people than you can imagine.

My internal partners in HR, Finance, Legal, E&C, Medical and so many others – know that I am thankful for your partnership and fully appreciate that any success achieved would not have been possible had we not moved forward together.

The leaders with whom I've worked have been incredible. I have been fortunate to be surrounded by those in Pharma that were both forward-looking and not risk averse. This allowed me to pursue my ideas. I point to this in Chapter Two as I started my journey. No better example exists than in my current work at Astellas. I have been given a platform to innovate and implement ideas across the organization. It began in 2019 when I spoke to the then-Chief Strategy Officer and now-CEO Naoki Okamura. From our initial video conversation to our in-person meeting in Tokyo it was clear Naoki was completely focused on the patient. Our discussion was remarkable in that every one of his leadership goals we discussed was first filtered through what was best for the patient. It was clear to me after those conversations that Astellas was where I wanted to further develop Version 2.0 of Patient Centricity. Since the beginning, Naoki has never wavered in his commitment and in fact has doubled down in many ways, supporting a cultural initiative globally and identifying the Patient Centricity function as one of three critical enablers of the Astellas strategic plan.

There are also members of Naoki's Leadership team who have been crucial in the implementation of Patient Centricity. While there are too many individuals to cite here, I will specifically mention three of them.

Chief People Officer, Katsuyoshi Sugita, is a leader who has supported the Patient Centricity function from the beginning. His patient first approach was evident when he addressed recruitment and retention, objectives and competencies for the organization – all in a patient centric way. This is a remarkable evolution that speaks to the intentional movement to a culture centered on our commitment to the patient.

Chief Counsel, Catherine Levitt, gave us the phrase "Patients are Waiting," which is just one example of the contributions she has made to this work through her outward support and quiet advice. It speaks solidly to her patient focus and leadership.

Adam Pearson, Chief Strategy Officer, has elevated the patient voice significantly within the organization – in a selfless and motivating way.His impact changed the dialogue for the better and has inspired many.

I want to thank my colleague and adviser, Gary Geipel, who supported this idea not only with words but with his valuable time and incredible guidance. I am forever grateful.

And, of course, to my collaborator, Don Hannaford, I have appreciated your patience, expert advice, feedback, and counsel. Your editing suggestions and subtle nudges have been superb and kept me feeling positive.

With respect to the many people with whom I've worked over the years: there are so many of you with whom I've shared ideas, concerns, and hopes. While some are referred to in Chapter 2, there are too many to name here. However, If we shared a conversation, discussed a challenge, or continue to connect regularly to share updates, I appreciate you and am thankful.

I will highlight the contributions of some individuals, whose decades-long support has been invaluable:

Peter Loupos who very early in this journey provided connectivity to patient groups and tirelessly supported this concept and the early efforts. He continues to be a leading voice for patient inclusion in medicine development.

Lana Skirboll, a friend, advisor, policy expert and one of the most politically astute people I've ever met. Many of our conversations helped me to navigate the minefields of progress.

Finally, my friend and colleague, Vicky DiBiaso. Vicky is a

world class clinical trial operations expert and an individual who is completely focused on the patient, working tirelessly toward a patient-centric clinical trial process. She was a very early collaborator in this work and we have had countless conversations over the years. I am truly fortunate to call her a collaborator and friend.

Printed in Great Britain
by Amazon

45843012R00099